P9-DYE-998

The Great Fair

Marc Chagall

The Great Fair

SCENES FROM MY CHILDHOOD

Sholom Aleichem

TRANSLATED BY TAMARA KAHANA

with a drawing of the author by Marc Chagall

THE NOONDAY PRESS *New York* *1955*

FOR MY CHILDREN—A GIFT

Dear, beloved children,

To you I dedicate my work of works, my book of
books, the song of songs of my soul. I realize that this
book—just as any man's handiwork—is not without de-
fect. But who knows better than you what it has cost me!
I have given to it of my best: *my heart.* Read it from
time to time. Perhaps you, or your children, will learn
something from it—to love our people and to appreciate
their spiritual treasures which lie scattered in all the
dark corners of our great Exile, in this great world. This
would be the best reward for my faithful, more-than-
thirty-years' labor in our mother tongue and literature.

Your father, the author,

Sholom Aleichem

NEW YORK, FEBRUARY 1916

Contents

Part I

1 Why "The Great Fair"?

IN LIEU OF AN INTRODUCTION. WHY HAS THE AUTHOR
UNDERTAKEN TO WRITE AN AUTOBIOGRAPHY? SHOLOM
ALEICHEM, THE WRITER, TELLS THE STORY OF SHOLOM
ALEICHEM, THE MAN.

When a man starts out for a fair, his heart is full of
hope; he does not know yet what bargains he may make
nor what his achievements may be. He flies toward it
like an arrow. Don't stop him—he has no time to dally!
. . . But after he returns from the fair, he has already
made his bargains, accomplished his achievements; he
is no longer in a hurry, for now he has plenty of time.
He is now able to sum up the result of his journey,
and he can tell about it unhurriedly, dwelling on every
detail: whom he has met at the fair, what he has seen,
what he has heard.

My friends have often insisted that I should recount
the story of my life. "The time has come," they said,
"and it may even be interesting. . . ." I tried to listen
to their advice. Several times I set myself to work, but
each time put the pen aside until . . . until finally the

right time came. Before I had reached the age of fifty, I had the honor of meeting His Majesty, the Angel of Death, face to face. I was almost dispatched to that place whence one cannot write letters nor even send a greeting by messenger. In short, having been practically gathered unto my forefathers, I said to myself, "Now the time has come. Snatch the opportunity and write, for no one knows what the morrow will bring! You may die suddenly. People who think they knew and understood you will turn up with cock-and-bull stories about you. What will you gain by it? Better do the job yourself, for nobody knows you as well as yourself. Tell the world what you are like, what you have done, what you have seen—write your autobiography! . . ."

It is easy enough to say *write your autobiography,* a truthful, unembellished story of your life. But it would be like giving an account of my entire life, or holding a confessional before the world! In fact, writing an autobiography and making a spiritual will are practically the same. Besides, it is difficult for a human being to rise to such a height that he can resist the temptation to show himself in the most flattering light, to paint himself as a "good fellow" who deserves a pat on the back. I have therefore chosen a special form of autobiography—that of a biographical novel. And so I shall speak of myself in the third person; that is, I, *Sholom Aleichem, the Writer,* shall relate to you the true life-history of *Sholom Aleichem, the Man,* as unceremoniously as I can, without embellishment or affectation, as an impartial observer might tell it, an absolute stranger—but still as one who had been with the hero

continuously and had passed with him through all the
seven circles of hell. And I shall tell it to you, little by
little, dividing it into separate stories or episodes. And
may He, who grants man the gift of Memory, grant me
this gift, that I may not omit a single occurrence of
interest* that I have experienced, nor one person whom
I have met at the Great Fair where I have passed almost fifty years of my life.

2 *The Village*

THE LITTLE VILLAGE OF VORONKO.   A KIND OF KASRILOVKA.
A LEGEND FROM THE DAYS OF MAZEPA.   THE OLD SYNAGOGUE,
THE OLD CEMETERY, THE TWO AFFAIRS.

The hero of this biographical novel was raised and bred
in Kasrilovka, which is already somewhat familiar to my
readers. It is to be found, if you are curious to know, in
Little Russia, in the county of Poltava, not far from the
old historic city of Pereyaslov. But its real name is
Voronko, and not Kasrilovka.

Strictly speaking, I ought to mention the city where
he was born and the date of his birth, as is customary
with biographers. I confess, however, that such details

---

* Sholom Aleichem lived to complete only the first two sections
of this autobiography.

have no interest for me. What does interest me is the little village of Kasrilovka—or Voronko—because no other town has so impressed itself upon my hero's mind as that blessed Kasrilovka-Voronko, and no other city in the world has endeared itself to him to such an extent that he cannot, nor ever will, forget it.

And come to think of it, what other city is there in the wide world—be it Odessa, Paris, London, or even New York—that can boast of such a great market place, and of so many Jewish shops, large and small; stands, of all sizes, stacked with mountains of freshly picked aromatic apples and pears, cantaloupes and watermelons, which goats and pigs are always trying to nip, so that market wives must constantly war against them? . . . And we, the schoolboys, certainly longed to taste these unattainable delicacies but could not come near them.

What other city contains an old humpbacked synagogue which has such a beautiful ark of the covenant carved with two lions that could be mistaken for birds, were it not for their long tongues and the rams' horns in their mouths? It was in this synagogue (so the old inhabitants tell us) that our grandfathers once locked themselves from the cursed Mazepa, the chieftain of the Ukrainian Cossaks; for three days and three nights they sat there wrapped in prayer shawls and phylacteries and read the Psalms, and that is how they escaped certain destruction. Those old inhabitants also tell us that the rabbi blessed the synagogue against fire; indeed, no matter how great a fire rages in the village, it never touches the synagogue!

What other city can boast of a bathhouse which

stands at the foot of a hill, on a river bank, and draws its water from an inexhaustible well? And the river! Where else is there such a river where generation after generation of Jewish schoolboys, as well as Gentile urchins, bathed, splashed, learned to swim, fish, and perform extraordinary tricks? Old Jews have plenty to tell about this wonderful old bathhouse. Once a peasant was found there who had hanged himself while drunk. This even led to a terrible calumny; the Gentiles claimed the Jews had hanged him. Oh, the village had trouble enough on its hands! They were prepared to whip the most prominent citizens—perhaps they actually whipped them, but I do not want to delve too deeply into this matter because I dislike sad stories, no matter how ancient.

What other city is graced by such a high hill, on the other side of the synagogue, the top of which almost reaches the clouds and where, as everybody knows, a treasure has lain hidden since the days of Chmielnicki —Chmielnicki, who led the Ukrainian rebels against Polish rule in the seventeenth century? Many times, we are told, people have begun to dig for the treasure, and each time have had to stop because human bones —legs, arms, skulls, and skeletons in shrouds—were turned up. These were obviously the remains of Jews, and perhaps even of martyrs . . . who knows?

In what other city will you find such excellent citizens? It may appear, at first sight, that they are no more than petty merchants and innkeepers living off the Gentiles and off each other. And yet they all behave with dignity; each has a home of his own, family prestige, and a pew in the synagogue—what difference whether it is at the east wall or the one opposite? And those who are less wellborn or less well off, no doubt have some distinguished relative of whom they can tell endless, exaggerated yarns. . . .

And what an old cemetery there is, what a large magnificent ancient cemetery where most of the graves are so overgrown with grass that no one is certain they contain human bones! You may be sure there are plenty of stories concerning this cemetery, and not very cheerful ones—in fact, rather terrifying stories of the past. But let us not talk of cemeteries before bedtime. . . .

This village of Voronko is small, but how lovely and appealing it is! If your legs are strong enough, you can walk its length and breadth in half an hour. You'll find no railway, no seashore, and no noise. . . . But it has two fairs a year, created specially so the Jews can carry on their trade and earn a living. A tiny, humble village —yet full of lovely stories and legends, enough to fill a whole volume! You are no doubt very fond of stories and legends. But we must keep within the limits of this biography, and so first we must introduce you, as is customary, to the father and mother of our hero. Be thankful that it is with his parents and not with his grandparents or great-grandparents, as most biographers do, that we begin.

3 In Father's Home

A tall man with a broad, white, wrinkled forehead, a
thin beard which seemed to smile, and a constantly worried expression! A man of means and an amateur cantor,
a scholar and a man well versed in the Bible, a pious
man and a lover of Hebrew, a disciple of the Hasidic
Rabbi of Talna, and a secret admirer of the more
"worldly" writers like Mapu, Slonimsky, and Zederbaum; philosopher, arbiter, counsellor, chessplayer, and
connoisseur of diamonds and pearls—this describes the
hero's father, Reb Nahum Vevik's [that is, Nahum, son
of Vevik], who was considered the richest man in town.

It is hard now to determine how great a fortune a
"rich" man could amass in Voronko, but occupations he
had in abundance. He was a lessee of properties, supplied beets to the sugar mill, ran the rural post office,
dealt in wheat, freighted barges on the River Dnieper,
cut lumber, and fattened oxen for sale. But his main
source of livelihood was the dry goods store. That is, it
was called a "dry goods" store, but besides dry goods,
one could also find groceries, hay and oats, homemade
medicines for the peasants, and even hardware. Father did not interfere in the dry goods store. It was man-

9

aged entirely by Mother, Haya Esther, a woman of character, an efficient, quick worker and a very strict mother. And of children there was no dearth—there were more than a dozen, of different sizes and complexions: black-haired, flaxen-haired, red-haired children.

Generally speaking, no one paid much attention to this host. They had not been greatly wanted, and, had they failed to enter this world, it would not have been considered a misfortune. But once they were there, then, "Who are they disturbing? May they have long and happy lives!" The ones who were lucky enough to get safely through smallpox, measles, and the other childhood diseases, were sent off to *cheder,* the Jewish school —first to Noteh Leib, who taught the youngsters, and afterwards to Reb Zorach'l, teacher of the Talmud. The child who did not escape the thousand-eyed monster which devours fledglings returned whence it had come. Then mirrors were draped; parents sat on the floor as a sign of mourning, their shoes off, weeping bitterly. They wept until . . . until they stopped weeping. They quoted the usual passages, "The Lord giveth, and the Lord taketh away," dried their eyes, rose from the ground, and—forgot. . . . In the constant noise and bustle made by more than a dozen children, one already married and sprouting a beard, another still an infant at the breast, it could not have been otherwise.

For the mother to rear such a host, to nurse each through illness, was quite a feat. A child received as many spankings, pokes, and slaps as he could absorb. But let him fall ill, and Mother did not leave his bedside. A mother's lot! And no sooner was the child well enough to leave his bed than, "Off to *cheder,* you rascal, off to *cheder!*"

Every boy attended *cheder* from the age of four until . . . almost until he was led to the marriage canopy. And it was the one who stood midway as to age in this horde who distinguished himself most in mischief—the hero of this biography, Sholom by name, or Sholom Nahum Vevik's.

Really he was not a bad boy, this Sholom Nahum Vevik's. Yet, although he surpassed the others in studies, he received the largest share of slaps and pokes and spankings. Very likely he deserved them.

"Wait and see, no good can come of this child! Look at him, obstinate, self-willed, greedy, growing up to be a good-for-nothing!"

So spoke Fruma, the pockmarked maid. Fruma was blind in one eye, but, nevertheless, she was a thrifty, honest, devoted servant. So devoted was she to her mistress that she took great pains to bring up the children to be good, pious, and devout in the eyes of God and man by whipping them black and blue and under-rationing their food. As Mother was a very busy woman, constantly occupied in the shop, it was Fruma the Maid who ruled the house with an iron hand and "educated" the children. She woke them, gave them breakfast, sent them to *cheder,* brought them back from *cheder,* slapped them, fed them, repeated the evening prayer with them, slapped them again, and put them to sleep in bed with her—that is, the children lay in the bed, and she lay at their feet.

Fruma the Maid was an enormous trial to the chil-

dren, and, when her wedding day came, they celebrated a great holiday. Long live curly-haired Yideleh
the Thief (he was a horse thief), who oiled his hair with
goose-fat and who could never properly blow his nose
because his nostrils had grown together! Blessings on
him, fool that he was, for deciding to marry blind
Fruma! And the truth is he didn't marry her just because
he didn't have "anything better to do," but "out of
love." He had been violently smitten by her, body and
soul. It wasn't because she had only one eye and a pockmarked face, God forbid, but because, by marrying her,
he became, in a sort of way, related to Reb Nahum
Vivik's. Such a match! That was no joke. Mother Haya
Esther herself arranged the wedding; she was the
bride's entire family: she baked the pastry, brought
musicians from the neighboring city, danced till daybreak, and finally became as hoarse as a crow.

How the youngsters laughed that day! What mischief
they made! Their joy was not due so much to the fact
that a noseless thief was marrying a blind spinster, but
because they were rid of Fruma's tyranny forever. They
also laughed because that rascal Sholom made them
laugh with his pranks: he imitated the bridegroom whistling through his nose, and the bride squinting at the
bridegroom with her one eye and licking her lips like a
cat that has just eaten cream.

Sholom was a master at mimicking others, at copying
their mannerisms and ridiculing their foibles. At his first
meeting with a person, he immediately discovered some
weakness—something "funny"—and he would mimic it
there and then. The horde would roar with laughter, but

his parents would complain to his teacher, "He's a regular monkey. We've got to break him of the habit."

And so his teacher undertook the task of "breaking him of the habit"—but with no appreciable result. A "devil" must have entered into the child, an imp intent on mocking everyone—absolutely everyone. Even the rabbi was included—his manner of taking snuff and of shuffling his small feet. And the rabbi's wife—the way she pursed her lips, blushed, and fluttered one eye when she asked the rabbi for money for the Sabbath, her way of mispronouncing the word "Sabbath," which came out always "Sabbas". . . . Hands struck, slaps resounded, rods whistled. Oh, those whippings! What whippings!

In short—some life!

4 *Shmulik the Orphan*

STORIES, FANTASIES AND DREAMS.   MAGIC AND THE KABBALA.

Some faces are created to bewitch you at first sight. Such faces cry out, "Love me!" And before you know it, you do love them.

Shmulik the Orphan had such an endearing face. He was a fatherless, motherless boy who was being raised by the rabbi.

Sholom Nahum Vevik's became attached to this boy from the moment they met. He shared breakfasts and lunches with him and they became friends—such friends! They were one being, one body, one soul. And all because of Shmulik's stories.

No one knew as many stories as Shmulik. It is not enough, however, to know stories; one must be able to tell them. And Shmulik told them best of anyone.

Where did this strange boy, with the red cheeks and dreamy eyes, get his fund of stories—lovely, fanciful tales, adorned with fantastic images? Did he hear them somewhere? Or were they all fruits of his fancy? Even now, I do not know. There is only one thing: they flowed out of him like water from an everlasting spring. They flowed as smoothly as oil. He drew them out like a long silken thread. His voice was sweet; his manner of talking was honey-sweet; his cheeks were red, eyes liquid and dreamy, as if veiled by a light mist.

On a Friday afternoon or Sabbath after lunch—sometimes on a holiday at twilight—having climbed the high Voronko hill "the top of which almost reaches the clouds," the two comrades would lie face down on the grass or look up at the sky, and Shmulik would begin his stories. One was about a king's son and a king's daughter; another concerned a rabbi and a rabbi's wife; still another was about a prince and a hunting dog; there were stories about a princess in a crystal palace, about twelve thieves in the woods, about a ship that sailed the "frozen ocean," about a pope who held religious disputes with great rabbis. There were stories about animals, devils, imps, evil spirits, magicians and sorcerers, wood-demons and werewolves, half-animals, half-men, and a story about the "hanging candlestick of Prague". . . . Every story had a smell and taste of its own; all of them were permeated with magic.

And Sholom Nahum Vevik's would listen openmouthed, never once taking his eyes off this wonderful boy with the red cheeks and the dreamy eyes.

"How do you know all this, Shmulik?"

"Dumbbell, you haven't heard anything. I know how to draw wine from a wall, and oil from a ceiling!"

"How do you do that?"

"Dumbbell, it's simple! I can make gold out of sand, and jewels and diamonds from broken glass!"

"How do you do it?"

"Why, with the Kabbala, of course. Didn't you know that our rabbi is a Kabbalist? Everyone knows that! He never goes to sleep."

"Well, what does he do?"

"All night long, when everyone else is in bed, he's up. He's all by himself, and he studies the Kabbala."

"You see everything he is doing?"

"How can I, dumbbell? I'm asleep."

"Then how do you know he studies the Kabbala?"

"How do I know? Why, even a baby knows that. Just ask! The rabbi can do the impossible. If he wanted, the twelve springs of quicksilver would open for him, and the thirteen gardens of saffron; and gold, silver, diamonds, and jewels, as many as there are grains of sand in the sea, could all be his. So many, you'd never want any more."

"Well, how come that you're always hungry, then?

And why doesn't the rabbi ever have enough money for the Sabbath?"

"Because! Because that's how he wants it! He wants to suffer in this world, do penance here. But if he wished, he could be as rich as Korah in the Bible. He could be richer than a thousand Rothschilds, because he knows how. He knows every secret. He even knows where the treasure is hidden."

"Where is it hidden?"

"Don't ask me! If I knew, I'd have told you long ago. I'd have wakened you in the middle of the night and said, 'Come, Sholom, let's get the treasure!' and we would have gathered the gold in our hands and stuffed it into our pockets. . . ."

And when Shmulik spoke of the treasure, his dreamy eyes glowed, his cheeks flamed, and he became so excited that his friend burned with the same fire. Shmulik spoke, and his friend Sholom stared at his mouth, drinking in every word.

5 Treasures

WHAT IS A TREASURE?   A LEGEND FROM CHMIELNICKI'S TIMES.   MAGIC STONES.

The fact that there was a treasure right here in our little village was indisputable.

How did we come by a treasure? Chmielnicki brought it, that Ukrainian who rebelled against Polish rule. Chmielnicki buried it here a long time ago. For thousands of years, people had been collecting treasure after treasure, and then Chmielnicki came and took them away and buried them.

"Who was Chmielnicki?"

"You don't know about Chmielnicki? Why, he was a monster, the Haman of his time. . . . Any baby knows that. . . . Well, this monster, this Chmielnicki robbed the nobles and wealthy Jews. He stole millions, and he brought it here, to Voronko, and buried it one dark night in the ground under the light of the moon, on the other side of the synagogue. The spot is now overgrown with grass, and a spell has been cast upon it so that no one can find it."

"So then it's lost for good?"

"Who says for good? Why do you think God created the Kabbala? The Kabbalists know a trick or two for this sort of thing."

"What kind of trick?"

"You can be sure it's the right kind. They have a magic spell where a certain verse from the Psalms must be repeated forty times forty. . . ."

"Which verse?"

"If I only knew! But even if I knew, it wouldn't help much. The way it goes, you have to fast for forty days, and you have to recite forty chapters from the Psalms on each of these days, and on the forty-first day, right after the sun has set, you've got to sneak out so that no one sees you, because if anybody does, God forbid, you have to start fasting all over again. . . . Well, if you make it and no one sees you—and it must be on a dark night, just before the new moon—you must go downhill to the other side of the synagogue, and there you stand for forty minutes on one leg, counting forty times forty, and, if you don't make a mistake in counting, the treasure will appear before you, just like that. . . ."

So, very gravely, Shmulik the Orphan would explain to his friend Sholom the secret of the treasure, and he would gradually lower his voice, speaking as if he read, not pausing for breath.

". . . and the treasure will appear through a small flame. When you see the flame, you have to walk up close to it at once. You don't have to fear getting burned because the flame only gives off light—it doesn't burn. Then all you have to do is lean over and gather in the treasure with both hands." (Shmulik would demonstrate how with both hands.) "You gather in the gold and the silver, and the diamonds and the jewels, and those precious stones called *Kadkod* and *Yashpoh*. . . ."

"What's the difference between those two?"

"Such a difference! *Kadkod* is a stone which throws light like a candle. And *Yashpoh* makes white out of black, yellow out of red, green out of blue, dry out of wet, a well-fed man out of a hungry one, young out of old, the living out of the dead. . . . All you have to do is rub it on the right hem of your jacket and say, 'Let a good breakfast appear before me!' And a silver tray will appear, and on the tray two fried pigeons and fresh white rolls, everything first class! Or else you say, 'Let a good dinner appear before me!' And a golden tray with all kinds of food and dishes fit for a king appears before you—right in front of your eyes are fried tongues and stuffed *kishke,* smelling deliciously, and fresh crisp *chalah,* and lots of wine of the best quality, and nuts and carobs and mountains of candy—such an enormous lot that you've had too much already!"

Shmulik would turn his head to one side and spit an excess of saliva. His friend would see by his dry lips and his pale dreamy-eyed face that Shmulik would not have refused a piece of fried tongue, nor a stuffed *kishke,* nor even a slice of white bread. . . . And he would make a vow that the very next day he would bring to Shmulik a few nuts and carobs and a candy stolen from Mother's shop. But, in the meantime, he would beg Shmulik to relate more and still more. Shmulik did not have to be coaxed. He would moisten his lips and speak on.

". . . and after you are stuffed with all these fine things, after you've drunk down the excellent wine, you take the stone, rub it, and say, 'Let a soft bed appear!' Immediately you have a bed of ivory, decorated with gold, with a feather quilt as soft as butter, and with silken pillows at the head, the whole covered with a satin blanket. You undress and fall asleep, and you dream of angels and cherubs, of seraphs of the Upper and Lower Paradise. . . . Or, if you prefer, you rub the stone, and suddenly you rise into the clouds and then above the clouds, and you fly like an eagle, way up, far far away. . . ."

Did the writings of his friend Sholom Nahum Vevik's, many years later when he had become Sholom Aleichem, reflect the spirit of this poor orphan with his wonderful stories? Who knows? One thing is certain— Shmulik had enriched Sholom's imagination, broadened his understanding, and to this day, deep in his heart, he treasures Shmulik's dreams and Shmulik's fantasies of riches and magic stones . . . although perhaps in a different guise.

6   *The Rabbi in Paradise*

THE FRIENDSHIP OF DAVID AND JONATHAN.   THE LEVIATHAN
AND THE SHOR-HABAR.   WHAT THE SAINTS LOOK LIKE IN THE
OTHER WORLD.

The wonderful stories of Shmulik the Orphan so completely enchanted his young friend that princes and princesses began to appear in his dreams. They shook him and pulled him by his sleeve, "Get up, Sholom, dress, and come with us! . . ." Even when awake, he would find himself among princes and princesses in a crystal palace, or on the frozen ocean, or on a desert island inhabited only by wild savages, or in the underground paradise where there are twelve springs of quicksilver and thirteen gardens of saffron, and where gold and silver lie around like so much dirt on the ground. Or by means of the stone *Yashpoh* he would rise high into the clouds. . . . This state of affairs reached the point where Sholom lost hold of reality and began to see all these wonderful things at every step.

It was sufficient for him to climb upon a pile of beams in the yard to become transported to a desert island and transformed into a prince. The ducks and geese strutting about the yard were the wild man-eaters over whom he ruled. He could do with them what he liked, and ordered them about at will since they were his humble subjects. . . . A piece of glass that he might find would immediately be transformed into a magic stone, a sort of *Kadkod*. . . . And who could tell whether the ordinary stone picked up from the ground was not called *Yashpoh?* When nobody was looking, he did not hesitate to rub it on the right hem of his jacket and say, as Shmulik said, "Let there appear before me. . . ."

But beyond anything, it was Shmulik's stories of the treasure that made the deepest impression on him. He was convinced that if not today, then tomorrow, he would find the treasure. He would, of course, give all the gold to Father and Mother. Father would no longer have to worry so about his affairs. Mother would not have to freeze in the shop day and night. With the magic of *Yashpoh,* he would build them a crystal palace enclosed in a garden of saffron, and in the midst of the garden would be a well of quicksilver. A hunting dog would guard the entrance, and werewolves, goblins, and wildcats would climb about the trees. And he, the prince, would generously distribute alms to the poor of Voronko, each according to his deserts.

Whoever dreamed that such inseparable friends as

Sholom Nahum Vevik's and Shmulik the Orphan would someday have to part forever? In the first place, why should friends ever part? Moreover, they had sworn in God's name, and confirmed their oath by striking the fringes of their *arba kanfoth* [ritual garments] over their hands, that one would never go anywhere without the other, and, no matter what happened to them or where fate might cast them, they would always remain one body and soul. It was such a love as that of David and Jonathan. But who could have dreamt that the rabbi, who was, I am afraid, not in the first flush of youth—in fact, was an ancient of seventy winters—would suddenly take to his bed and give up his ghost, and that the orphan, Shmulik, would go with the rabbi's widow to a little village, heaven knows where, and would disappear just as if Shmulik had never existed!

To be sure, all this did not happen as quickly as it takes to tell. A rabbi does not lie down and die so easily. He, who had always been frail and sickly—partly because of too much fasting and partly from undernourishment—finally took to bed in his old age. For over a year he lay paralyzed without eating or drinking a thing—only studying, praying, and struggling with the Angel of Death. Shmulik swore to his friend with all kinds of oaths that every evening at twilight, between the two evening prayers, "That One" flew in through a crack in the window, stationed himself at the rabbi's head, and waited to make a grab for his soul should he ever stop praying. But the rabbi was too clever for him. Not for a single moment did he stop praying—he simply went on praying and studying, studying and praying.

"What does he look like?"

"Who?"

" 'That One.' "

"How should *I* know?"

"You said he comes every night, so you must have seen him."

"Stupid! Anyone who lays his eyes on 'That One' won't live to tell about it! How could I have seen him?"

"Then how do you know he comes?"

"What do you think he does? Sit in the sky waiting for an invitation?"

The day of the rabbi's death was a holiday for the two friends. The rabbi had a beautiful funeral such as only a small-town rabbi can permit himself. The shops were closed, the schools deserted, and the "whole city" accompanied him to the cemetery.

On their return home, the two bosom friends, "David and Jonathan," were the last in the crowd. They walked slowly, holding hands, so that they could have a good talk. There was plenty to talk about: the rabbi's death and his arrival in the next world; how he would be met at the gates of paradise; how he would be greeted; and who would be there to receive him.

Shmulik knew everything—even what went on *there.* And he talked about it as though he had been there himself. It was this way: the rabbi did not really die. He merely transported himself to another world, a better world, where he was greeted with the finest delicacies of paradise: the Leviathan, the Shor-Habar, and ancient sacred wine. Ah, only *there* will he have his first taste of a good life, a happy life—in beautiful Eden, among such aristocrats as Abraham, Isaac, Jacob, Joseph the Righteous, Moses and Aaron, King David and King Solomon, the Prophet Elijah, and Rambam, Baal-Shem-Tov, and the Tzadik of Rijin. . . .

How lifelike they became when Shmulik described them, and how real they seemed, each so distinctive in face and character! Father Abraham was an old man with a white beard; Isaac was tall and lean; Father Jacob, frail and bent; Joseph was "a beauty"; Moses our Teacher was short in stature, but his forehead was broad. On the other hand, Aaron the Priest was tall and he carried a long knobbed staff; King David had his fiddle; King Solomon wore a golden crown; Elijah the Prophet was a poor little Jew; Rambam—the great sage Maimonides—had a round beard and was dressed in finery; the saintly Baal-Shem-Tov was an ordinary Jew with an ordinary stick in his hand; the Tzadik of Rijin was a very handsome man and wore a white silken cassock. . . .

You felt you wanted to see all these people with your own eyes. You longed to join them in paradise, to taste just a bite of the Leviathan and the Shor-Habar, and only a drop of the sacred wine. You actually envied the rabbi who was now having such a good time. You quite forgot that only a short while ago he was lowered into a dark narrow grave, covered with sticky black earth, slapped down with wooden shovels, and that Shmulik himself had said *Kaddish* [the prayer for the dead] because the poor rabbi had died childless and left no one behind to pray for his soul.

7 Shmulik Disappears

DAVID AND JONATHAN ARE PARTED FOREVER.   THE SECRET OF THE LOST TREASURE.   LOST, A FRIEND.

Throughout the entire week when the rabbi's widow observed the mourning rites for her late husband, Shmulik the Orphan wandered about the village, solitary, like an orphan who has lost his parents twice over. Throughout the day he looked forward to the evening when the children would no longer be at *cheder;* then he would meet his friend, Sholom Nahum Vevik's, who, after the rabbi's death, became even more deeply attached to him. The two bosom friends, "David and Jonathan," sensed that they would soon be parted. They did not yet know how, nor did they want to know. Nevertheless, they tried to spend every evening as much together as possible.

Fortunately, it was summertime, and during the summer one does not attend the *cheder* in the evenings. They would therefore go to Nahum Vevik's garden and spend a few hours chatting under the pear tree. Or else, they would wander far out of the village, beyond the mills, so long as the peasant brats did not attack them and sic their dogs on the "damned little Jews."

Beyond the mills, the two friends could talk to their hearts' content. And there was plenty to talk about.

There was one thing that interested both of them: what next? What if Shmulik had to go away, for Shmulik had heard that the rabbi's widow was preparing to leave for some distant town in the county of Kherson. She had a sister there who had invited her to come and stay. If the rabbi's widow left, Shmulik had to go with her, for how could he remain here all alone? He hadn't even a place to lay his head!

It was understood that, if he went, he would not go for long—at any rate, not for forever. The moment he arrived there, he'd start studying the Kabbala at once. And, as soon as he discovered the "secret," he'd return to Voronko and begin the job of looking for the treasure. He would fast forty days, recite forty chapters of the Psalms every day, and on the forty-first day he'd sneak out, so that no one would see him, and count forty times forty standing on one leg, forty minutes by the watch. . . .

"When did you get a watch?"

"I don't have one yet, but I will."

"Where will you get it?"

"Why, I'll steal it! What do you care?"

Sholom looked into his friend's eyes; he was afraid he had offended him and that he would become angry. But Shmulik was not the sort whose friendship hangs on a single word. And Shmulik continued telling stories about the future when they would both be grown up and big men; the things they'd do in the village; how happy they would make the Jews of Voronko. Honeyed words flowed from his lips. In the warm summer night, neither wanted to stir. But they had to. They had to go home to bed, or else they'd catch it. They would take leave of each other, "Until tomorrow, until tomorrow. . . ."

So one "tomorrow" passed and then another and still another—and then there was no Shmulik! Where was he? He had gone. He had left suddenly with the rabbi's widow for the county of Kherson. When? How? Without even a goodbye!

His friend Sholom was miserable and forlorn. He felt deserted—as solitary as a pebble. Gone was his best friend, his dearest, his most beloved! The whole world seemed black to him. What was the world to him without Shmulik? Life became meaningless. What was life without Shmulik? And the lonely, forsaken friend felt a contraction in his throat; something began to tickle in his nose; something pricked at his heart. He hid in a corner and wept long and bitterly.

Can he still be alive, this curious dreamy-eyed Shmulik with his wealth of enchanting tales? Where is he? What has become of him? Is he now a preacher—a rabbi —a teacher—a merchant—a shop-keeper—a broker? Or is he simply a miserable wretch, the poorest of the poor? Perhaps he has drifted to that golden land, America, where he is "making a living"? Or perhaps he has already finished his task in this world and has gone to that other world where dreams come true?

Whosoever has heard anything of him—please let me know.

27

8 Meyer Medvedefker

A NEW, MUSICAL FRIEND.   THE CHILDREN PLAY "THEATRE."
A BAREFOOT SCAMP TURNS INTO A FAMOUS SINGER.

The bereaved friend was not left to mourn Shmulik very long. God took pity and compensated him by giving him a new comrade.

This is how it happened. After the old rabbi's death, the village was left without a rabbi. Nahum Vevik's put all business aside and went to Rakitna, another village, which was famous for its rabbi, who was called Chaim Medvedefker. Nahum Vevik's brought him to Voronko, and the village celebrated the event, for, besides being a great scholar and a God-fearing man, and besides being endowed with an excellent voice, he was very poor; so to make ends meet he agreed to tutor the eldest children of wealthy families.

You must not think, however, that Reb Zorach'l, who had been the teacher up until then, was deprived of his students. How could one take a man's livelihood away from him, just like that? So Reb Zorach'l continued to teach the smaller children; he taught them the Bible and penmanship and Yiddish, Russian, German, French, and Latin, of which neither the teacher nor the pupils could make head nor tail, while the new rabbi taught the Talmud to the older boys. And despite the fact that

Sholom Nahum Vevik's refused to grow, he was admitted to the higher class, for no sooner had the new rabbi examined him in the Pentateuch and Rashi's Commentaries than he pinched his cheek and exclaimed, "What an imp!" and told his father it was absolutely sinful for such an imp to be left to poke around only in the dry old Bible; he should be given the Talmud as a treat. "Don't worry, he can digest it!"

Father naturally was overjoyed, and the imp was pleased also. He wasn't delighted so much by the Talmud as by the prospect of sitting among "big" boys. He was puffed up with pride and he carried his nose in the air. This was nothing to joke about!

Reb Chaim, the rabbi from Rakitna, did not come alone. He brought two sons with him. One, Avremel by name, was already married; he had a big Adam's apple and a good singing voice, and already prayed before the altar. The other, Meyer'l, also had a good singing voice and an Adam's apple, but, as far as studies were concerned, he was a dunce. Actually, he was more mischievous than stupid, and it was with him that Sholom Nahum Vevik's quickly struck up a friendship. A boy all the way from Rakitna, and a rabbi's son—that was nothing to sneeze at! Moreover, Meyer'l had a special talent: he would sing songs, and what songs! It is true that, with this quality, he also had a failing, the weakness of a true actor: he did not like to sing "just for the fun of it," that is, free of charge. You want to hear me sing? Be kind enough to pay for it! A penny, a song. And, if you haven't any money, an apple will do. If worst comes to worst, half an apple, a couple of plumes, a candy, but no payment, no song! Yet he knew very beautiful songs, and he sang them very sweetly and with great feeling:

> At night I walk about the street
> And hear a cry so dolorous.
> They cannot sleep, they wail and weep:
> 'Oh, woe to us! Oh, woe to us!'

The children listened open-mouthed to him, melting with pleasure—and he, the nightingale, remained cool and unmoved. He could also intone prayers like a real cantor. Once, when the rabbi Reb Chaim, his own father, left the room for a minute, Meyer'l wrapped himself in a tablecloth for a prayer-shawl, took a position facing the wall, pinched his throat with two fingers like a cantor, and let out a wail from the prayer of Atonement, "God, the King who sits enthroned. . . ." Then, just as he had got warmed up, the rabbi returned.

"What's this! Playing cantor? All right, you renegade, stretch out on the bench. . . ."

And his execution began.

Meyer'l Medvedefker was distinguished not only for singing. He had another weakness—acting. He liked to dress up and do "The Sale of Joseph," "The Exodus from Egypt," "The Ten Plagues," "Moses with the Tablets," and so on.

Sometimes he would be a robber, with a great stick in his hand and his mother's kitchen knife stuck into his father's belt, trousers rolled up—and barefoot, naturally. And his eyes—real robber's eyes! Sholom Nahum Vevik's was the Jewish beggar. A thick staff in his hand, a cushion for a hump, his cap turned inside out, the poor wretch would walk about begging alms. He would get lost in a forest, the trees of which would be represented by the rest of the children. So Sholom Nahum Vevik's the Beggar would wander among the trees, leaning on his staff, looking for a path out of the forest, and he would meet . . . Meyer the Robber! The robber would snatch his knife out of his belt and would sing a song—in Russian, naturally—ending with:

> Out with the money!
> O-o-o-out with the money!

Sholom the Beggar, tears in his eyes, would entreat the robber to be merciful, to take pity if not on him, then on his wife and children. His wife would be left a widow, and the children would become orphans. But Meyer the Robber would seize him by the throat, throw him to the ground, and . . . the rabbi would appear, and the fun would start.

"It is true," and he would point at his son, "that we have here a no-good renegade . . . but *you,* the son of Nahum Vevik's, what are you doing in the company of this turncoat?"

Reb Chaim evidently was something of a prophet. Many years later, his son Meyer Medvedefker (by this time the famous opera singer, Medvedeff) actually did "turn," that is, he became a convert. But we must hasten to add that he fulfilled the commandment "Honor thy father" as though he were the best and strictest of Jews. He bought for the poor old man a house in Rakitna, showered gold upon him, and visited him every summer, bringing gifts for the whole family. Reb Chaim, who never learned the trick his son had played on him so that he might be styled "Artist of the Imperial Theatres," lived to a happy old age. . . .

But let us return to childhood when Meyer'l Medvedefker did not know nor even dream that he would someday be called Michael Ephimovich Medvedeff, and take cities by storm and conquer the world.

9 Crime and Punishment

PICKING PEARS.   LESSONS IN THEFT.   THE NINTH OF AB IN
THE PRIEST'S GARDEN.   THE PUNISHMENT.

It was not surprising that the two cubs, Meyer Medvedefker and Sholom Nahum Vevik's, became fast friends. They had much in common, and both had a vague premonition that someday, something would come of them. Nor was this premonition altogether false. When they met some twenty years later, in Belaya Zerkov, a city in the county of Kiev, one was the famous singer Medvedeff, and the other had already written articles in *Dos Yiddishe Folksblatt,* under the pseudonym, Sholom Aleichem.

But let us return to their childhood when one was

still called Meyer'l Medvedefker and the other, Sholom Nahum Vevik's, and when they still walked the streets of Voronko barefoot, like all other children of good families. To be quite candid, we must admit that neither had a strong love for that knowledge which their teacher, Reb Chaim Medvedefker, attempted to hammer into them, nor for the piety he tried to instill. They preferred other things—such as plucking gooseberries from the bushes, or shaking pears and plums from the trees; even though the fruit grew in one's own garden, it was more fun to pick it than to languish over the Talmud, praying piously or reciting the Psalms, as Reb Chaim required of his pupils.

"The Talmud's no goat—it won't run away. God will forgive an unsaid prayer, and, as for the Psalms, they're for the old."

This is how Meyer'l Medvedefker argued with his friend Sholom, and taught him instead how to climb in a flash the tallest tree and how to jump and catch hold of a branch of the wild cherry; then the cherries slipped into one's mouth of their own accord; one's lips became black, and one's fingers bore witness to one's iniquity. What of it? "So we'll be whipped! Who cares?"

To receive a whipping at school was such a usual event that the youngsters experienced no feeling of shame—as for the pain, why mention it? "If we do get a few whacks from the teacher, it'll heal by the time we're married!" It was embarrassing only for those boys who were already engaged; they were afraid that their fiancées might learn about it—or, even worse, that their fiancées might be teased by their girl friends: "You have a bridegroom with a sore . . . you know what!"

As Meyer was not engaged, he had nothing to fear, and he led his friend Sholom along the primrose path. He taught him how to "swallow" a prayer, and how to filch carobs and other candies from the shop, right under Mother's nose. Naturally, this was not actual *stealing*—it was *taking*, and one is not punished for this in the next world. . . .

Everything might have gone along smoothly if an accident had not overtaken Meyer. One day he had the misfortune to climb over a fence into the priest's garden, and while he was gathering pears the priest's daughter caught sight of him from the window. She called her father, and he hastened out with a dog and the culprit was caught. The dog tore his trousers; the priest threw away his cap, and then released him to the four winds.

This might not have been considered so dreadful if it had not taken place on the Ninth of Ab, the day commemorating the destruction of the Temple in Jerusalem. Imagine the scene: the Jews are walking about in their stocking feet, weeping and wailing the destruction of the Temple, and he, the son of Reb Chaim, the rabbi, promenading bareheaded, in torn trousers!

The punishment the unhappy youngster had to undergo cannot be described in these progressive days. Nor was this the worst of it. Nahum Vevik's was forced to remove Sholom from the *cheder*, and other parents, following his example, also removed their children. And so Reb Chaim, the rabbi, was left without students. Since the position of rabbi and cantor brought him little, he had to return to Rakitna, and once more the village was left without a rabbi.

But do not fear, it was not so for long. Nahum Vevik's brought a new rabbi from Borispol. His name was Shmuel Eli. A young man, Shmuel Eli was a good scholar, a fine singer, and, in addition, played an excellent game of chess.

He had only one failing. He was somewhat addicted to intrigue and flattery. Also, he enjoyed talking to young women when no one was looking. . . .

And that was how our hero lost his second friend.

10 Silver

AN INTELLIGENT, RESPECTFUL DOG. COMPASSION FOR ANIMALS. A TRANSMIGRATED SOUL. A FAITHFUL FRIEND.

Sholom had yet another friend in those days, a third whose memory will remain with him forever. Were it not for fear of offending the other two, I would say that the third was the best of all, the most dearly loved, and certainly the most faithful. His name was Silver. The name itself is sufficient to indicate that this friend was not human, but a dog, an ordinary dog with a gray coat and hence the name "Silver."

I have said "ordinary," but I must withdraw the word, for, as we shall soon discover, he was no ordinary dog. But first we must devote a few words to this dog's biography—for how did it happen that a Jew owned a dog?

When Nahum Vevik's moved out of the city to the village and took over the rural post office, together with its courtyards and all other appurtenances, he discovered Silver, still a very young but already intelligent puppy, in the yard. Silver was so clever that he immediately acknowledged his new masters. Moreover, he treated Jews with respect; he did not worry them like most dogs, who boil with hatred as soon as they see the long Jewish gabardine.

Of course, Silver was not intimate with his new masters. In fact, he was never allowed to show his nose within the house. From the very first, it was made quite clear to him, with the help of a piece of fire-wood, that a dog has no business inside a Jewish home.

Nor was he allowed admission to the kitchen. One-eyed Fruma the Maid exiled him forever with a pitcher of boiling water which she affably poured over him one Sabbath eve, burning a patch into his coat.

Oh, that Fruma! There was a woman with the heart of a Tartar. She could bear the sight of neither dog nor cat. Once, with tears in his eyes, Sholom Nahum Vevik's barely managed to rescue from her clutches the cat which she had tied to the leg of a table and was beating so mercilessly with the broomstick that the screams of the unhappy creature must have reached the very gates of heaven!

"Fruma, darling, sweetheart, pet, what are you doing! Don't you have any feeling for animals? God will punish you! Hit *me* instead, hit me, but not the cat!" And Sholom presented his back to the despotic maid. Finally, realizing herself that she had treated the cat too brutally, she poured a pitcher of cold water over it and just managed to resurrect the half-dead creature.

Now what do you suppose was the cause of all this fuss? It seemed to Fruma that the "glutton" (she had no other name for the cat) must have stolen something because she had found it licking its chops. "Now why should a cat start licking its chops all of a sudden?" Fruma suspected everything and everyone; a cat had to be a glutton; dogs were mischief-makers; every peasant was a thief; every child, a pig.

But let us return again to Silver. Another dog might have left thus shamefully driven from the house and the kitchen: "Goodbye and good luck!" But Silver was different. Even had he known he was risking his life by remaining, he would not have left the yard. This was where he had been born, and here he would die. . . . Moreover, he found good advocates in the master's children. He won their hearts despite Fruma's best efforts to slander him. Many a dog might have envied the sweet and easy life Silver enjoyed. The youngsters smuggled to him, in their pockets, the best of everything—secretly, of course, else it would have gone ill for both dog and children. Silver knew the time for breakfast, lunch, and supper and impatiently awaited the hour when the good things to eat would arrive. He even knew who was carrying food and in what pocket it was hidden, and immediately his muzzle would seek out the right spot. What a rascal that dog was!

And the tricks the youngsters taught him! When you put a little bone or even a piece of bread on the tip of his nose and said to him, *"Nie roosh!"* that is, "Quiet!" (naturally, you speak Russian to a dog), he would wait diffidently as long as you wanted, until he heard the welcome word, *"Hamm!"* that is to say, "Eat!"

Winter nights, when the children were at *cheder,* Silver would wait for his comrades impatiently. Every evening, about nine, he would appear underneath the school window and scrape at the frozen panes with his paws. That was the signal to close one's books and return for supper. Silver was the teacher's clock. "I'm sure a human soul has entered that dog," he would say, and then he would let the children go. Off they went, carrying their paper lanterns greased with fat, and happily singing merry Russian songs:

> One, two, three, four,
> Hurry, scurry through the door!
> Five, six, seven, eight,
> Helter-skelter through the gate!

or

> It's time, it's time
> To say farewell!
> To all your friends
> Sing, "All is well!"

Silver ran ahead of them, leaping for joy, rolling in the snow—all for the sake of a piece of bread and a little bare bone for supper!

When his heart was heavy, when his spirit was low, when he had got it good and proper at home and even worse at school, Sholom Nahum Vevik's often retired with Silver into the further recesses of the garden, far beyond the trees. There, on a rubbish pile heaped against the fence, he would sit with his faithful Silver, who, with muzzle extended, would stare into his eyes. "Why does he stare like that? What is he thinking about? Does he really understand, just like men do? Has he actually got a soul, like people?" His teacher's words would come to Sholom's mind: "A human soul has entered that dog." And he would recall what King Solomon had said in Ecclesiastes, "A man hath no preeminence above a beast."

"If there is no difference between them, why is Silver a dog and I a human being?" Sholom would muse, and he would look at the dog with compassion, a compassion not unmixed with respect; the dog would return his gaze as though he and the boy were equals.

11 Silver's Tragic End

AN UGLY CALUMNY.   THE END OF AN INNOCENT DOG.
BITTER TEARS.

I do not exaggerate when I say that Silver was an intelligent dog, a dog who knew who loved him best, and it was therefore no wonder that he became more attached to the author of these memoirs than to any of the other children. The friendship between them was a silent one. Silver adored Sholom; he could not live without him and was ready to lay down his life for his friend and master. Although he was a dumb animal, incapable of voicing his love in words, he managed to express it in his canine way by jumping, yelping, and rolling on the ground in front of his young master. All his friend and master had to say was, "To your place!" and Silver would retire decorously, lie down as quietly as a kitten, and keep one eye fixed on his master's movements.

It was a quiet love between "master and slave," and the master could not picture life without Silver. Could Silver ever cease to be? Was Silver a human being that he could go away with a "fare-thee-well?" How often did peasants attempt to lure Silver to their village! The very next day he would come running back, panting, his tongue hanging out, and would throw himself down, roll on the ground, then jump into his master's arms, yelping and licking his neck. One could have sworn there were tears in his eyes. . . .

And yet there came a day, a dark unhappy day, when Silver suddenly left—and for ever and ever in a way that was ugly and unjust.

The month of July witnessed this sad event. It was a summer of terrible drought. There was not a drop of rain. Many people fainted from the heat. And it is well known that during heat waves, dogs become dangerous —they can go mad.

A rumor spread through the village that a dog had gone mad and had bitten other dogs, but no one was sure which dog it was. The villagers were panic-stricken. Their first thought was to insure small children against being bitten.

This precaution consisted of sending all the children to old Trophim, a peasant conjuror who had sharp nails with which he could "remove the little blue dogs from under the tongue" so skillfully you didn't feel a thing. The operation was not dangerous, but it was scarcely pleasant to have a peasant thrust his fingers into one's mouth and search for "little blue dogs."

Next they turned their attention to the dogs. They brought from heaven knows whence two huge brutes, dogcatchers armed with stout ropes and iron hooks, whom they immediately put to work. In a single day, the two executioners took care of several dozen dogs. Their claim was that they could distinguish at sight between a mad dog and a healthy one. Who ever dreamt that good, clever, peaceful Silver was to be among the chosen?

The villagers must have paid the brutes per head for every dog they destroyed. If so, there must have been many another innocent victim besides Silver.

It was only after the deed had been done, on their return from *cheder*, that the children discovered the calamity. They staged a revolution. "Silver! Silver! How could you allow it!"

To be sure, the revolution was put down by a counter-revolution. "Who ever heard of schoolchildren making such a fuss about a dog!" Their parents rewarded them with a bountiful portion of slaps, and for dessert brought the matter to the attention of their teacher, begging him not to spare the rod. This favor he was only too happy to grant. The rod was not spared.

None of this mattered greatly. What did matter was that poor innocent Silver had perished so unnecessarily.

Silver's favorite took it hardest of all. For several days, he did not eat or sleep. At night he tossed from side to side, groaning and sighing, nor could he forgive the cruel, evil people who felt neither conscience nor pity nor sympathy for animals. And again he fell to thinking of the difference between dog and man. Why was a dog so faithful and why was man such a tyrant? . . . And as he thought of Silver and his bright, clever eyes, he threw himself on his pillow and wept.

12 The Spirit of Good and the Spirit of Evil

LECTURES.   A SUPERFLUITY OF GUARDIANS.   SNUB-NOSED
OZER, THE INFORMER.   GRANDMA MINDE'S SABBATH TREAT.
THE POWER OF THE SPIRIT OF GOOD AND THE SPIRIT OF EVIL.

The boy might have forgot that he had once had a dog
for a friend had he not been reminded of it at every
step. Grown-ups would tease him, "Silver sends his regards . . ." and they would throw in a lecture for good
measure to take care of the future. These lectures were
worse than any punishment. To quote the proverb, "A
blow is forgotten, a word is remembered." Moreover, in
this instance he had his share of both blows and words.
He was inundated by words. They came from every
side. Every God-fearing and well-meaning person felt it
his duty to scold the boy.

One could well ask why a beadle should be concerned
with a rich man's son at prayer time. What business is
it of his that the boy looks through the window while
the Eighteen Silent Benedictions are being read? Do
you suppose that a boy looks through a window for no
good reason? The Eighteen Benedictions may be very
noble indeed, but it is much more interesting and in-
structive to watch an unusual event—a dog chasing a cat.
The cat bristles and flies off like an arrow shot from a

bow, the dog after her. The cat leaps from the fence, the dog in pursuit. The cat runs to the water pipe, the dog still trailing her. The cat climbs the water pipe to the roof, and the dog stops, nonplussed. The canine remains standing foolishly, licking his chops, evidently thinking the matter over. "Why should I, a dog, chase a creature not my equal? And is there anything worth doing on top of a roof?"

"Is this how one says the Eighteen Benedictions?" Melach, the beadle, asks, and he grabs the boy by the nape of the neck. "Just wait, you rascal, till I tell your father!"

Or take the case of snub-nosed Ozer, once a shoemaker, now turned bath-keeper in his weary old age. What business was it of his if the sons of Nahum Vevik's slid down hills and ripped their trousers? Naturally, snub-nosed Ozer had to witness this from the bathhouse window, and he had to go trumpeting through his nose, "Rafcalf, fcampf! A plague upon your anfeftorf! It fayf in the Bible 'Do not deftroy!' Taking brand-new pantf and fpoiling them! Your fchoolmafter will hear about thif!"

For those who do not understand the subtleties of nasal speech, we may translate it thus:

"Rascals, scamps! A plague upon your ancestors! It says in the Bible, 'Do not destroy!' Taking brand-new pants and spoiling them! Your schoolmaster will hear about this!"

To complain to the teacher was considered not only an act of kindness, but a solemn duty all were obliged to perform, since everyone had children of his own. It was therefore incumbent on them all to keep an eye open and assist in the upbringing of everyone's children, if not by means of the hand, then by way of the tongue. That is why the children had so many guardians and were so surfeited with lectures, sermons, and admonitions. There was a continuous buzzing in their ears: "Don't do that! That's no place to stand! No, don't go there!" Everyone buzzed: Father, Mother, sisters, brothers, teacher, servants, uncles, aunts, Grandmother—especially Grandmother, who deserves a few words all to herself.

Grandma Minde was a tall, well-groomed woman, neat and pious to a fault. Her special concern was to make sure that her grandchildren grew up to be observant, God-fearing Jews. So she moistened the tips of her fingers with her tongue and straightened the boys' earlocks; she dusted and smoothed out their clothes and heard their prayers morning, noon, and night. In return for all this, it was obligatory for the boys to visit her every Saturday afternoon to wish her good Sabbath. They sat along the wall and decorously awaited their "Sabbath treat." No one received too much of this "Sabbath treat," but it was served on clean, shining plates. The treat usually consisted of a small apple and a peach and a piece of carob and either a fig, or several withered raisins. Along with the treat came interminable lectures. From these lectures one gathered that one must obey one's parents and indeed all God-fearing people, that it was most important to be a good Jew, and, if you weren't, God would punish you. He would punish you for missing a prayer, for being disobedient, for not studying, for any little trick you happened to play. He would even punish you for an evil thought or a spot on your coat. . . . And very soon you lost all interest in the apple and the peach and the carob and the withered raisins. . . .

But Grandma Minde's lectures were nothing compared to those sermons that poured from the mouth of the teacher those very same Sabbath afternoons, just before the evening prayer. So vividly did he describe the Spirit of Good and the Spirit of Evil, Eden and Gehenna, the Angel of Hell, and the flinging of sinners from one end of the world to the other that he drew rivers of tears from the eyes of his audience! He saw swirling at the feet of his students a thousand imps and demons. They were encompassing the children. They were in the folds of their clothes, were even under their fingernails. He was convinced that every boy of them was a candidate for Gehenna. For, said he, even if a boy had committed no sin, even if he had said all his prayers and studied diligently and abided by all the commandments of the Spirit of Good, yet at some time he must have succumbed to the Spirit of Evil by *intending* to sin! And even if he never had intended to sin, he must certainly have had a wrong thought, or at the least seen something sinful in a dream!

No, there was no escape from the Spirit of Evil; better lie down and die! Was it not spite that kept one alive? Spite made you play tricks, it made you laugh, eat candy, "swallow" your prayers, and think of forbidden things. So it was doubtless the work of the Spirit of Evil and his multitude of assistants luring the innocent into his net. And poor unfortunate, once he is caught, against his will he must obey and, like a little calf, do everything the Evil Spirit bids. Most unfortunate of all, the Spirit of Evil is extremely lucky. Everyone obeys him more readily than his opponent. Lectures and admonitions do not seem to do much good. On the contrary, the more the Spirit of Good tries, the more successful is the Spirit of Evil. I am afraid that, if there was no Spirit of Good, the Spirit of Evil would have no employment. . . .

13   Theft, Cards, and Other Wickedness

HELPING MOTHER AT THE FAIR.   CARD-PLAYING IN HONOR
OF HANUKAH.   BERL, THE WIDOW'S SON, GIVES STEALING
LESSONS.   THE END OF A RENEGADE.

The Spirit of Evil was particularly successful with the children of Nahum Vevik's. Not only did they swallow their prayers, forgetting to say more than half of them; not only did they shamelessly lie to Grandma, saying that, in addition to their prayers, they had read several chapters of the Psalms—but, as if this were not enough, they also learned to steal, to stuff themselves, and to gamble. . . . Naturally, all of these transgressions were not committed simultaneously; one misdemeanor followed another, just as the Scriptures say, "One sin draweth another."

As I have already said, the Jews of Voronko gained their principal livelihood from the peasants, particularly during the two great fairs. The fairs were looked forward to eagerly, and when the day came the entire village was busy. Everyone was occupied—trading, bartering, bargaining, selling. The peasants—particularly the women folk—were as busy as anyone. What they were busy at was stealing. No one was safe from those women. No sooner had a shawl or a ribbon been retrieved from the sleeve of one woman than another had managed to snatch a candle or some candy from under your nose. What was to be done? Mother Haya Esther devised a plan: she stationed her sons in the shop to watch out for thieves. So, rascals that they were, they did their level best. Not only did they stuff their pockets with cake and tobacco, nuts, and prunes, but they kept a sharp watch over the green cash box. No sooner was Mother immersed in conversation with a customer than they would slip a few "coppers" into their pockets, and then, at the first opportunity, off they would run to *cheder*. There they would spend their ill-gotten gain. They would buy pancakes, biscuits, peas, poppy-seed cakes, sunflower seeds—or else they would gamble.

Playing cards was a sort of disease in Jewish schools, and it was epidemic in character. It would begin on Hanukah and continue throughout the winter. Everyone knows that playing games on Hanukah is an act of virtue. Some boys play with the *dreidl* [a kind of top] and others play cards.

Of course, I do not mean *real,* printed cards—God forbid! The cards I refer to are homemade, "Jewish" cards intended for the game called "Thirty-one." But it is all one: the same Tempter officiates, and the same excitement is generated. When Hanukah comes around, even the teacher joins in, and he does not mind winning all his students' Hanukah money. To lose your Hanukah money to your teacher is an honor, a joy, a pleasure. In any case, no one will disagree that it is better to lose to your teacher than be whipped by him.

But with the end of the holiday came the end of cards. The teacher sternly proclaimed, "Now remember —if anyone touches a card, if he speaks about cards, if he even thinks about cards—he's as good as whipped!"

The teacher apparently had once been one of the boys himself and had liked to gamble, and not always in honor of Hanukah—or else how could the thought have entered his head? . . . But the fact remained that the pupils continued to play cards long after Hanukah, indeed throughout the winter, and with even more excitement and fervor than during the holiday. They gambled away breakfasts and lunches. Whoever had a few pennies lost them on cards, and those who had nothing sought in every conceivable manner to obtain the wherewithal to play.

With the help of a waxed straw, some pulled pennies from the poor-box of Reb Meyer the Miracle Maker— pennies still wet with the tears of the mothers who dropped them into the box every Friday evening before blessing the candles. Some children managed to save a few pennies from the commissions they earned by running errands, and others got hold of Father's or Mother's purse at night, when everyone was asleep, and took as much as they dared. They did this with great trepidation and under great risk. And all the money was spent on cards!

The important questions were when and where to play so that the teacher would not find them out. It was the older students who arranged things, boys like Eli Keila's, the red-headed owner of a silver watch and already engaged, and Berl, the widow's son, a lad with thick lips and teeth so strong that he could bite through iron. Berl was already growing a beard, and he himself was responsible for it, he informed his friends; it was because he smoked. "Here's the proof," he pointed out, "when you begin to smoke, you begin to grow a beard!" He taught many boys how to smoke cigarettes and how to obtain the necessary materials, or—to put it more bluntly—how to steal. Naturally, Berl was paid for his instructions and payment was made in tobacco and cigarette paper.

Berl had a system all his own. Those who obeyed him and brought him tobacco and cigarette paper were "good guys," "regular fellows"; but those who were afraid, or couldn't bring themselves to steal, he regarded as "sissies" and "babies." They were barred from his company and, if necessary, he beat them. To fight back or to inform on him was out of the question, since one would thereby be giving oneself away, and there were few heroes. And so the children did whatever Berl the Widow's Son commanded, and along with him they sank deeper and deeper into the abyss.

Heaven knows where they would have ultimately ended up if Berl had not accomplished his own undoing. The children were too young and innocent to understand quite what had happened. All they knew was that the crime had taken place on a Friday and that the boy had been caught behind the bathhouse where he had removed some of the glass from the window and had been peeking at the bathing women. . . .

Oh, what a rumpus there was in the village! His mother, the widow, fainted. Berl was expelled from school and was not allowed to enter the synagogue. No decent child was permitted to associate with this "renegade," as he was thereafter called. And as if to live up to his name, years later, when his mother was no longer alive, Berl the Widow's Son became a convert and was no longer heard from.

14   Feigeleh the Witch

THE WINNERS REPENT.   GIRL OR DEMON?   A TICKLING WITCH.

You must not, however, suppose that the Spirit of Evil always had the upper hand. One must not forget the month of Elul during which come the Days of Repentance, *Rosh Hashonah* and *Yom Kippur*. Moreover, any number of prayers, fasts, and penances have been invented by godly people. If one disregards petty thefts and card playing and other childish transgressions, it can truthfully be said that Sholom Nahum Vevik's was actually a good boy. Pious and God-fearing, he often vowed to himself that when he grew up he would be much better; he would become as good and as pious as Grandma Minde and teacher, as all God-fearing people expected him to be.

How often he wept during his prayers! How often he sought to avoid his older brothers and all the other wicked companions who incited him to evil! And when the Days of Repentance came around, the Fearful Days, he was deeply penitent.

Oh, it is very sweet to be pious and good. Only those who themselves have done penance can testify to the fact that there is no finer experience in the world. A penitent is one who has reconciled himself with the Almighty; he has triumphed over the Spirit of Evil and communes with the Divine Spirit. What can be more wonderful than reconciliation? What can be sweeter than victory? And what can be dearer than the Divine Spirit? A penitent feels that he has become clean, strong, and whole; he has been born anew and he can look everyone straight in the eye. Ah, yes, it is good, it is exceedingly good to be repentant!

As soon as the month of Elul arrived and when the ram's horn was first sounded, it seemed to our hero that he saw the Spirit of Evil lying bound hand and foot, squirming on the ground and begging for mercy. And what of *Rosh Hashonah?* What of *Yom Kippur?*

Enduring the difficult fast, the hunger, the deathly thirst, controlling oneself like an adult—in these experiences he found the sweetness, charm, and beauty that only the pious, or those who have once been pious, can appreciate. What pleasure can compare with leaving the synagogue weary with fasting, purified of all one's sins, one's soul completely cleansed? One looks forward to the meal at home, anticipating the divine taste of honey-cake dipped in strong brandy and . . . but stop! What's wrong? The Jews have paused to bless the new moon! "To be sure, we are hungry and tired and weary, dear Lord, but this shall not prevent us from blessing your moon!"

Oh, how good it is to be a Jew, a godly Jew, a repentant one!

And yet, the Spirit of Evil, cursed Satan, always interfered and ruined everything! And this time, Satan appeared disguised as a village girl, a girl with curly hair and green eyes.

An ancient tradition required that every year during the Fearful Days, country Jews, or "holiday people" as they were called, come from surrounding villages to Voronko. Every citizen had his special "holiday people." Nahum Vevik's guest was a distant relative, called Lifshitz the Gluboker (because he came from the village of Gluboky). He was a pious Jew and possessed a broad forehead—the forehead of a sage, although in fact he was not blessed with an excess of brains. His wife was as pious as he; she had two loves, praying and taking snuff. The couple had no children, only a servant girl, called Feigel, who was an orphan and distantly related

53

to them. The children gave her another name: they called her Feigeleh the Witch, because she looked more like a demon than a girl. She behaved like a boy, preferred to play with boys, and when nobody was looking she would tell them strange stories and sing them songs, most of them in Russian.

Once, on a warm moonlit night, during the Feast of the Tabernacles, she stole to the place where the boys were sleeping. To make room for the holiday guests, the children had been put to sleep in the yard on the ground. She sat down among them, half-naked as she was, loosened her braids, and began to tell her eerie stories. They were not such stories as Shmulik had told. Hers were tales of demons, of goblins and imps who turned clothes inside out, shifted furniture about, leafed through books, broke dishes, pulled pots out of ovens, and performed other odd pranks. There were also stories of witches and sorcerers. A witch, she told the children, could torture a hundred people to death merely by tickling them.

"Tickling? What do you mean?"

"Don't you know what it feels like to be tickled? Let me show you how witches tickle!"

And Feigeleh the Witch with her wild face and disheveled hair showed them how witches tickle. At first the children merely laughed; but then they began to resist and fight her off. They pulled her hair and slapped and kicked her. Feigeleh pretended to defend herself, but it was obvious that she was enjoying the beating. She did not attempt to run from them, and it was apparent she craved for more. . . . Her face burned, her eyes—light green, catlike—glistened. In the light of the moon she seemed a real witch. But the worst of it was that the witch overcame them all, embraced each one in turn, crushed him to her breast, and kissed every boy, kissed him full on the lips!

Fortunately, this happened before *Hoshana Raba,* the last day of purification, before the reckoning is complete in Heaven, so that one had time to appeal to the Lord not to consider these stolen kisses as a very great sin.

Who was Feigeleh the Witch? What sort of creature was she? Was she a spirit, a demon, or a werewolf? Or did the Tempter himself assume a woman's form in order to lure innocent children against their will into the sin of kissing a girl?

15 *The Hobgoblin*

THE MISCHIEVOUS POLTERGEIST.   THE HOBGOBLIN IS CAUGHT.
A LOOSE GIRL IS MARRIED OFF AND BECOMES A PIOUS WOMAN.

The identity of Feigeleh the Witch was soon revealed in a manner so unexpected that it is worthy of being recorded.

That very winter, during the holiday of *Hanukah,* Lifshitz came from his village with the news that a hobgoblin had settled in his house, a sort of *Poltergeist* who was making his life miserable. At first, the hobgoblin simply played tricks on them: every night he thumbed through the folios of the Talmud, tore the prayer books and the Bibles to shreds, overturned the dishes in the cupboard, broke the pots, threw the phylactery bag into the slop pail together with the picture which hung on the eastern wall, and turned the portrait of Moses Montefiore face to the wall. And you didn't even hear a rustle! After a while, the hobgoblin started to turn pockets inside out, empty them of their contents, and steal the small change that was kept in the table drawers. It even threw his wife's pearls away! What a plague, what a pest! And now he, Lifshitz, had come to his relative for advice. What was he to do? Should he complain to the authorities? Should he go to the Talna Rabbi for counsel? Or should he simply leave the village of Gluboky?

After listening carefully to the whole story, Nahum Vevik's asked two simple questions: "Where does the servant girl sleep? How does she get along with her mistress?" Lifshitz was almost offended. First, Feigel was related to them; his wife intended to marry her off and even give her a dowry; she was very happy with them. Secondly, she slept like a top in the kitchen with the door locked.

"Has she any friends in the village?" asked Nahum Vevik's. This question made Lifshitz really angry and he started to shout, "Where can she find friends in a village full of peasants? Perhaps you think that Feigel is the hobgoblin?"

"God forbid!" replied Nahum Vevik's, laughing up his sleeve at his simple relative. He tried to prove to Lifshitz that imps and hobgoblins do not exist, but the man would not even listen. He swore—if it was a lie, let him not live to hear the Messiah's trumpet-call—that at night he himself had heard some living creature snort and scrape with its fingernails, and, on the very next day, he had seen peculiar traces of chickens' feet on the sand-covered kitchen floor!

When Nahum Vevik's realized whom he had to deal with, he turned, as the saying goes, the shafts around; in other words, he altered his tactics. It was, of course, quite possible that the hobgoblin was an honest-to-goodness hobgoblin. Still, he would like to see it with his own eyes. If Lifshitz agreed, he could take Nahum with him to his village so that he could have a look at it for himself. . . . And, if Nahum went, his younger brother Nissel Vevik's ought to go along, too.

"My brother Nissel," Nahum explained, "is a real man. He's terribly strong, knock on wood. He has already taken care of the village sheriff, and we have reason to hope, therefore, that he'll be able to cope with your hobgoblin. . . . Are we going?"

"With the greatest pleasure!" Lifshitz agreed joyously and taking time by the forelock, the three of them, well bundled up in warm bearskin coats, settled down in a wide sleigh and were off to Gluboky.

They arrived in the village at night and were very hospitably received. A dairy supper was served in their honor, and they whiled away the time discussing the hobgoblin.

Later, while Feigel was serving at table, Nahum told a tall story concerning the Rabinowitz family. He assured them that from birth all of the Rabinowitzes had slept a remarkably deep sleep. You could carry them out to the street, bed and all; you could shoot at them with cannons—they wouldn't wake up! On the other hand, they had no fear of evil spirits, neither devils nor imps, even when they were carrying money on them. That was because they were no fools; they kept their money sewn in their underclothes, and they never took their underclothes off. As a matter of fact, they did not even believe in the existence of hobgoblins or devils or witches or any of that nonsense. They were invented by our enemies, and only fools believed in them!

Lifshitz's naive reply to this was that it would not be a bad idea if the hobgoblin paid them a visit that very night—then they'd know whom they had to deal with! . . . The whole evening was spent talking in this vein. Wine was called for, and both brothers pretended to get drunk. Then everybody went to bed, the lights were extinguished, and the guests soon made themselves audible by snoring, one outdoing the other—it was a real concert!

Suddenly, about midnight, there was a terrible racket—a struggle going on. Strange voices were heard shouting Yiddish and Russian. The Lifshitzes jumped out of bed, trembling with fear; they put on the lights and saw the following spectacle: in Nahum's arms lay Feigeleh the Witch, bound hand and foot, yet still struggling. Nissel, the strong man, was wrestling with Feodor, the district scribe, who had bitten Nissel's hands to the bone. But finally Nissel overpowered him and tied him up like a sheep. At daybreak, they took the culprits to the village police station. There they presented the village counsellors with two bottles of vodka and the following decision was reached: Feodor, the district scribe, was to confess all and return everything he had stolen from the Lifshitzes with the girl's help. If that was done, he would be let off easily; that is, they would keep quiet about the affair, and he wouldn't get much of a whipping.

As for the girl, they dealt very handsomely with her. To turn her over to the Gentiles was out of the question, even though she was a witch, a loose woman. . . . All they demanded of her was to tell them what she had done with the pearls and other articles she had stolen. They gave her their word of honor that she would be shipped off to the city and married as soon as possible. She would have a fine wedding, with musicians, a trousseau, and a wedding dinner—such as the purest Jewish girl would get. As for this nasty affair, "No bird would hear of it, since no rooster would crow."

And that is exactly what happened. They found her a fine fellow. He was a ladies' tailor called Moshe Hersh. The Rabinowitzes were the matchmakers and the kinsfolk. The entire village attended the wedding; even the authorities were there. They did away with enormous numbers of bottles of wine and beer, and it was something to see Nissel Rabinowitz dance with the sheriff.

After the wedding, it was difficult to recognize Feigeleh. She became as pure as a rabbi's wife. She would not look at a man, and toward Nahum Vevik's children she behaved as if they had never been introduced. When charity was to be collected for the poor, she was the first to take a kerchief and make the rounds.

But as one thing had nothing to do with the other, her girlhood name, "Feigeleh the Witch," remained with her forever. It was Nahum Vevik's boys who saw to that—particularly he who was neither the oldest nor the youngest, the biggest rascal of all, the author of these memoirs.

16 *Vevik's Sons*

THREE BROTHERS, THREE CHARACTERS.   REB PINNEY THE
HASID.   A SOCIAL WORKER'S SALARY.   HOW TO DANCE
ON CANDLES.

Nahum Vevik's, the father of our hero, had two brothers, Pinney Vevik's and Nissel Vevik's, whom we have already mentioned. Strangely enough, none of the brothers resembled one another in the least; each was a distinct type. The eldest, Nahum, was, as we already know, a mixture of a Hasid and worldly man; he was a philosopher and a lover of prayer, a scholar of the Bible and a student of literary style; he was by nature modest, secretive, and very melancholy. The second,

Pinney Vevik's, was an extremely observant Jew and wore an exceptionally long ritual garment known as *talith katan.* He was a fine figure of a man with a handsome face, a handsome beard, and handsome laughing eyes. Very lively and energetic by nature, he was always busy with social affairs; he was a skillful *mohel,* that is, a circumciser—not for money, perish the thought, but for the sake of piety. He was a fiery man, forever immersed in other people's business, court trials, arbitrations, quarrels, claims, and peace-making, and always occupied with the affairs of widows, orphans, and the poor. He was, in addition, a trustee of the synagogue and of the Burial Society, the head of a group which studied the *Mishnah* [Jewish traditional laws] and of a group which read the Psalms. I suspect these occupations meant more to him than the business which he conducted at the market or the fairs. His varied interests cost him dear, but what did it matter when there was a good deed to perform? On the contrary, the more the cost, the finer the deed, and, if one complained, an act ceased to be benevolent!

In short, another person's business, anything that smacked of communal affairs, everything that constituted helping a fellow Jew, took precedence. He would leave the market or the fair to go running to a circumcision ceremony. The circumciser was, naturally, no one but himself. Or else he would hurry off to arrange the wedding of a poor orphan and dance all night long with her poor relatives—here surely was an opportunity to be kindly which did not often present itself.

One cannot help but wonder where this pious, God-fearing Hasidic Jew learned to dance so well! Who could have taught him? His specialties were "The Hasid," "The Cossak," and "The Russian."

"Quiet, please! Reb Pinney Vevik's is about to dance The Hasid!"

"Make room! Reb Pinney Vevik's is beginning The Cossak!"

"Women, step to one side! Reb Pinney Vevik's will demonstrate The Russian!"

Every space would be cleared for him, and Uncle Pinney would dance The Hasid, do The Cossak, or demonstrate The Russian to the gaping audience.

The poorer the wedding, the greater the merrymaking. That is, the poorer the bride, the wilder Uncle Pinney danced. And he would perform tricks that were really extraordinary—and all out of kindness—so as to amuse the bride and groom. It was worth a good deal to see Uncle Pinney dance "on candlesticks" with burning candles, or "on a mirror." He did it as lightly and as gracefully as a professional dancer.

Uncle Pinney would throw his coat off, pull his *talith katan* out, roll up his sleeves, his trousers tucked into his boots, his feet barely grazing the ground, his head thrown back, and his eyes shut. Ecstasy and inspiration would illuminate his face as at prayer. The musicians would play a Jewish tune; everybody would clap to the rhythm; the circle would gradually widen; and the dancer, balancing among the burning lights, became more ecstatic and more inspired as he proceeded. . . . It was not dancing. Rather it was a kind of divine service, a holy rite!

But we have allowed ourselves to be carried away by the subject of dancing and have, in the meantime, forgotten the third brother, Nissel Vevik's, to whom it will be necessary to devote the next chapter.

17 Uncle Nissel and Auntie Hodel

UNCLE NISSEL MAKES MERRY. AN INTIMATE OF THE AUTHORITIES. A PLAGUE OF A WIFE. GETS INTO TROUBLE. THE POETIC SPARK.

Whereas the two elder brothers, Nahum and Pinney, were pious and serious people, their youngest brother Nissel Vevik's—or, as he was later called by his family name, Nissel Rabinowitz—was a merry, frivolous, democratic man of the world, everybody's favorite. Even in his dress he differed from his brothers; he dressed like a dandy with a slit in his coat-tails (this was called "German style" in those days); he brushed his earlocks carefully behind his ears, wore a white starched shirt and patent leather shoes. But should anybody suppose he was not a law-abiding Jew, he would be mistaken. Nissel was a God-fearing Hasid, like his brothers; it was just that he didn't make a fuss about it. In the synagogue, he had his honorary place at the east wall with all the other well-to-do parishioners, but he would also often go into the vestibule and sit next to the stove with the simple folk. He used a Bible with rather advanced commentaries and told the common folk yarns about Moses Montefiore and Rothschild. An added attraction was his pleasant voice and his talent for singing. He loved to laugh, and he knew how to make others laugh—especially women and young girls. It is hard to say why he affected them so. One word from him would throw them into gales of laughter.

What a gay dog he was! Without him a wedding was a funeral. Nissel Rabinowitz could raise the dead. He could get a whole crowd of people to chattering, laughing, and dancing. Between him and Uncle Pinney there was this difference: Uncle Pinney knew how to dance; Uncle Nissel knew how to make others dance. At a party, everyone drank with him, sang with him, danced with him. The sheriff would be the first. He and Uncle Nissel would exchange caps, and the merriment would begin.

Nissel Rabinowitz was friends with the authorities, and so ruled the village as if he were a functionary. He was, moreover, a good talker and spoke Russian like a Slav. Even the Gentiles respected him. *"Khodim do Miselia; vin i dilo skazhe, i charka horilka bude!"* "Let's go to Nissel's; he'll give us some advice with a glass of vodka thrown in!"

He liked, even more than Uncle Pinney, to try his hand at communal matters. He was forever at law for someone or with someone, and he was certain he knew all there was to know about the law. A Jew who spoke Russian like a native was someone to be reckoned with!

On such good terms was he with the authorities he would slap the elder of the village if it was necessary, would tipple with the head of the borough, would embrace the sheriff as though they were blood brothers.

But Uncle Nissel, a mighty figure to the villagers, was far from a mighty figure to his wife. No great man is! Auntie Hodel was a small dark woman, but what fear she inspired in her huge husband!

It was odd to see tall, broad-shouldered Uncle Nissel, so respected by the authorities, who spoke such good Russian, who was always so well dressed and merry, this cavalier, this guest ever welcome among women—it was odd to see him protect himself from a pillow thrown at his head or a wet broom smacked across his elaborate embroidered coat. His "little" wife liked to "sweep him with her broom," particularly on holidays, and especially on *Simchath Torah* [the Feast of the Rejoicing of the Law] and preferably right in front of everyone. "Let all know what sort of husband this is!" He would turn all these tribulations into a joke. He would lock himself in the hall with the men, open endless bottles of brandy which he served with sour pickles stolen from the cellar; all the pots and pans would be taken out of the oven—in short, the house would be devastated! For three whole weeks thereafter he would be hounded by Auntie Hodel. But the spree would have been worth it.

All the more curious that Uncle Nissel would undertake nothing without first consulting Auntie Hodel. He regarded her as a woman of brains. He would say, in her defense, "She comes from the city of Korsun—and all Korsuners are hot-tempered." He would also say, "There's only one remedy—pearls!" Could he manage, with the help of God, to buy her a string of pearls, her character would alter completely.

"I know a better remedy," his elder brother Nahum said with a faint smile, and whispered something in Nissel's ear which made Nissel jump as though he had been stung.

"God forbid! Absolutely not!"

"Take my advice, Nissel. Do as I say, and everything will be fine."

What Nahum's advice was came to light much later. Auntie Hodel published the secret throughout the village, punctuating it with curses directed against her husband's family. "What a fine family that is! Let them strike women if they wish, but their hands will wither away before one of them touches me!"

The whole town knew that Auntie Hodel led Uncle Nissel a dog's life, though he was a mighty man and a friend of the authorities. Indeed, it was being a man of influence that led him to play a trick which altered the whole course of his life and the lives of his children and grandchildren. I suspect that this story is apocryphal, but I shall tell it, nevertheless, as it was told to me.

In a small town not far from Voronko—I believe it was Berezan—the peasants decreed that a certain Jew was to be expelled from the village. What was to be done? Posthaste he sought out Nissel Rabinowitz, who spoke Russian so fluently and who was on such affectionate terms with the sheriff. Uncle Nissel rushed to the sheriff, but the sheriff pronounced himself helpless. The chief of the county was the man with influence. Now this chief was, to begin with, just newly appointed, and a veritable Haman besides. But could one let a Jew be ruined and an entire family be left destitute? "Wait a bit, *budet dielo v shliape,* everything will be all right! We'll find a way," Uncle Nissel said, and perpetrated the following ruse. He obtained the uniform of an official, dressed himself up like the chief of a county, caught the postchaise, and arrived in the village, wheels rumbling and carriage-bells ringing. The elder of the village and the whole council were summoned, and then Uncle Nissel proceeded to shout at them, "How dare you, you so-and-sos! . . ." He stamped his feet like a real official, fuming that it was not "according to the law," and then he tore the decree up into little pieces. If they dared complain to the governor, he warned, they should bear in mind that he, their new chief, was related to the governor on his mother's side, and moreover his wife was somehow related to the minister of the interior and the exterior.

It is not known who informed on him. The story of the torn decree, along with the governor and the "minister of the interior and the exterior" leaked out, and a warrant was sworn out. Uncle Nissel was arrested, convicted, and imprisoned. And, later, brave Uncle Nissel had to take to his heels and flee for his life. For a while he dallied in Odessa, where, at last, he secured a false passport and, under a false name, took off with his family for America—sailed all the way to Canada! There they had a hard time at first, but, some years later, letters reporting that they were "making a living" began coming from him. These were followed by handsome pictures in which everyone looked like lords and barons. . . . But precisely how one "made a living," and precisely what life in America was like, could in no way be discovered from them.

The portrait of Uncle Nissel is incomplete if we omit one more characteristic: perhaps a poet was lost in this man. He used to sing Yiddish songs of his own composition, and while he was in prison he wrote a song about himself in which every line started with a letter in alphabetical order. Moreover, he composed a pretty, haunting melody for it. How many unknown talents are thus lost among us!

18 Pinneleh Shimeleh's Goes to Odessa

THE CENTER OF THE UNIVERSE. SHIMELEH, A JEW WHO SPEAKS RUSSIAN TO THE JEWS. STARTS OUT FOR ODESSA. PINNELEH KNOWS ALL ABOUT THE WORLD. THE AFFAIR OF THE PEA. THE FAREWELL SUPPER. THE CENTER OF THE UNIVERSE TOTTERS.

In those days the hero of this biography, like perhaps every Jewish boy, considered his village the heart of the universe, the very navel of the globe; his fellow Jews were the Chosen People of God; leading the Chosen People were, of course, the Rabinowitz children; and the very crown and pride and jewel of the Rabinowitzes was his father, Nahum Vevik's. For who sat in the most exclusive pew of the synagogue, second only to the rabbi, right next to the Ark of the Law? Whom did one visit first on a holiday? At whose house were there gatherings every Saturday evening to take leave of Queen Sabbath with wine, song, dance, and merriment that lasted till daybreak? Truly, in the whole family there was no finer man than Nahum Vevik's, nor any home more prosperous. No man was more pious than Uncle Pinney, none merrier than Uncle Nissel. . . .

Looking at his tall father, dressed in a handsome silk coat with a broad belt and a tricornered hat on his head, which he wore on Sabbaths and holidays; or watching his little mother, Haya Esther, when she raised her delicate white hands to bless the candles in tall puffed silver candlesticks; or listening to his tall neat Grandma Minde talk with God as with an intimate friend; or hearing Uncle Nissel, the strong man, gabble Russian like a real Slav—Sholom Nahum Vevik's would feel proud and happy. He thanked the Lord for his good fortune in being born into such a family, in feeling contented as a prince and secure as in a royal fortress.

But suddenly the pillars of the fortress began to shake, the palace toppled, and all the charm of the happy village dissolved in an instant. The young "prince" discovered that Voronko was not the navel of the globe—there were many other larger cities, and much wealthier men than the Rabinowitzes. All this he discovered from his new friend, Pinneleh Shimeleh's, whom we shall now briefly describe.

Besides Vevik's children, the Rabinowitzes, there was in Voronko another wealthy Jew, Shimeleh by name. He was a compact little man with a small round belly, a pleasant, constantly smiling face, and a slightly crooked mouth. He was more prodigal than wealthy. A ruble meant nothing to him. He spent as much as he earned and, when he was down to his last penny, borrowed more and spent it all over again.

The villagers considered him a freethinker because he wore a cape and his beard was suspiciously short. On the other hand, he distributed alms liberally and, when the desire seized him, would summon guests in the middle of the week and throw a party in high style.

Shimeleh preferred Uncle Nissel to the other Rabinowitzes. Like Nissel he wore a coat slit in back, cut off his earlocks, and liked to speak "Russian" to the Jews—which meant he peppered his Yiddish with Russian words and phrases. Also, he had an exceptional handwriting, since he was left-handed; as everyone knows, "lefties" write beautifully. He was always a guest in his own home, for he could be found there only on holidays; then, as soon as the celebrations were over, he would depart again, laden with so many gifts that the whole village ran wild with excitement and gossiped about them for months afterwards.

Once, just before Passover, he returned from one of his journeys and spread the news that he was leaving Voronko for good. Where to? Oh, far, far away—as far as Odessa! "Only cattle," said he, "are content to remain in this mudhole! If you were to visit Odessa, you'd know what a *real* city is like! If you only saw Ephrati's warehouse and all his employees! The money that passes through that warehouse in a single day, you and I should wish for ourselves, you sons of Belial!"

Needless to say, everyone listened to Shimeleh openmouthed and marvelled about Ephrati's office and the money that passed through it in a single day. But behind his back they jeered at him and that famous warehouse—Shmuel Eli especially. Shmuel Eli was the new rabbi and cantor, a clever young man, insolent and sly, fresh from the city of Borispol. He said, "You can thumb your noses at Shimeleh! First of all, he isn't going anywhere. Secondly, if he does go somewhere, it won't be to Odessa, but much closer—probably to the town of Rezhishchev—and not because the people of this village are cattle, but simply because he is so deeply in debt, he can't call the hair on his head his own!"

Whether he was going to Odessa or Rezhishchev, whether because of the cattle or the creditors, nevertheless Shimeleh appeared to be in earnest. Right after Passover he put his household goods on sale for half price. Many of his things he gave away as gifts. He dressed his daughters like brides, and from Israel, the tailor, ordered short jackets for his sons, suitable for a city the size of Odessa. And, in order to make the village bubble even more, he ordered his wife, Henya, to give a party and fry cheese *blintzes* for the entire community.

Naturally, not a soul stayed away from the party,

and in fact the first to arrive was Shmuel Eli, the new rabbi and cantor, who had made a laughingstock of Shimeleh behind his back and now sickeningly flattered him to his face.

The youngsters came along with the adults. But, instead of sitting quietly and decorously inside the house with all the guests, they chose to remain out-of-doors, close to the wagons, in order to watch them being loaded for the departure. There Sholom Nahum Vevik's found Pinneleh, Shimeleh's youngest son, a boy with a preoccupied expression and large protruding eyes. They climbed into one of the wagons, settled down on the driver's seat, and began to discuss the approaching journey.

Pinneleh Shimeleh's was, at that time, Sholom's closest friend. Sholom liked him because he knew everything that went on in the world, for, besides having heard all the stories his father told about big cities, Pinneleh had actually visited one himself. He had been to the city of Pereyaslov due to that business of the pea.

To explain the affair of the pea, we must say a word about Pinneleh's character. He was a thoughtful boy with an inquisitive and experimental mind. For example, he pondered over the fact that watches tick and crinolines stand of their own accord. So he decided to investigate. He cut up his mother's crinoline into little pieces and pulled his father's watch apart. He got what he deserved both from his father and his mother; he accepted the punishment with good grace, but he did not profit from the accompanying lectures.

One Sabbath evening, his mother was shelling peas. Pinneleh watched her at work and suddenly realized that peas were round. He took one pea in his hand and began to muse on the nature of peas. Why were peas round and not square? He thought so much about it that he decided to perform an experiment. He put the pea into one ear and tried to pull it out of the other.

His intentions were good—it was a pure experiment. But the results were unfortunate. Once inside the ear, the pea refused to budge. Pinneleh went off to *cheder*. He friends took the matter in hand and tried to pry the pea out of his ear; one of the boys stuck his pinky in; another tried to get the pea out with a broom straw. But nothing worked. Pinneleh returned home for lunch. His mother noticed that the child had lost his appetite and asked, "Pinneleh, why aren't you eating, and why do you look so sad?"

She didn't leave him in peace until he had made a clean breast of it. When his mother learned what he had done, she was beside herself. What did she do? First of all, she gave him a couple of slaps, so that a child should know better than to stick peas into his ears. And then she took him by the hand and brought him to the teacher, who added a few smacks of his own. When the punishment was over—and not before—they put him to bed, and the teacher, the teacher's wife, and all the neighbors started to pour water into one ear and pry with an iron wire in the other.

"Pinneleh, tell us at least into which ear did you stick the pea?"

But Pinneleh did not reply. Apparently, in all the

excitement, he had forgotten into which ear he had put the pea and out of which ear he expected it to emerge. Pure reason, however, told them it must have been the right ear. Why the right ear? "Because it's human nature. People use their right hands more than their left." (This was the teacher's opinion.)

But his wife had an exactly opposite theory. "What good is pure reason and human nature when with the wire I can feel the pea in the child's left ear!"

"In that case," the teacher asked, "would you mind telling me how the pea got into the left ear?"

His wife replied, "Why ask *me?*"

"So whom should I ask?"

"Ask the pea!"

In the end, they had to take Pinneleh to the doctor who lived in the big city of Pereyaslov and there—as Pinneleh told the story—with a pair of pincers they took his ear apart and removed the pea. And, by that time, the pea had grown. It had turned green, grown roots and sprouted leaves!

Pinneleh had plenty to tell about the journey to the big city, and, in the eyes of his friends, he grew a whole head taller. It was no joke for a boy to have visited Pereyaslov and to have seen with his own eyes hundreds of houses roofed with tin, sidewalks on every street, white churches with green domes and golden crosses, shops made of stone, mountains of cantaloupes and watermelons, countless apples and pears literally littering the ground like so much refuse, soldiers who marched in the street, and many, many similar wonders.

From that time on, Pinneleh Shimeleh's and Sholom

Nahum Vevik's became fast friends, and his departure was for Sholom a greater blow than for anyone else. In addition to the feeling of jealousy, because Pinneleh was going away and not he, he found it difficult to part from a friend whom he had learned to love no less than his former comrades.

When he came to say goodbye to Pinneleh, Sholom found the lucky boy handsomely dressed and groomed. He stuck his hands into his pockets like a grownup and started to make fun of Voronko. "What is Voronko? A wilderness, a ditch, a mudhole, a tiny village—it's worse than a village! And the people! They're paupers, beggars, ragamuffins! All the Jews of Voronko taken together, even counting the wealthy ones, don't earn as much as Ephrati earns in Odessa!"

Then Pinneleh began to boast of how they would soon ride away in the wagons with bells ringing and dust flying; what a wonderful, long trip they would have; how they would arrive in Odessa; how all the great people would come out to greet them, carrying fresh rolls, fried geese, and cherry wine, and Ephrati would be there to receive them, too. . . .

"Who is Ephrati?" Sholom asked him.

"Don't you know who Ephrati is?" Pinneleh replied, just like a grownup. "He is related to us on Mother's side. He's a wealthy man, a capitalist, a millionaire! I've already told you, dumbbell, all that the Voronko Jews earn together won't add up to what Ephrati keeps in one coat pocket. You can imagine how rich he is—he rides with six horses drawn tandem and has an equerry galloping in front! He dresses in silk and velvet from head to foot, and he has two fur coats, one made of bear, the other of fox. And on weekdays he eats nothing but rolls and fried goose and drinks only cherry wine. . . ."

"And what'll you do there?" Sholom asked him, swallowing at the mention of fried goose and cherry wine.

"Such a question!" Pinneleh answers seriously and with assurance. "What do other Jews do in Odessa? What does Ephrati do? Ephrati has a wheat warehouse of his own, and my father will have a warehouse. Ephrati has an office full of people, and my father will have an office full of people; money will simply roll into our pockets. Odessa's no joke!"

Pinneleh began telling about Ephrati's greatness and Odessa's beauty—Odessa, with its three-storied buildings. "Compared to Odessa, dumbbell, our town is— what shall I say?—it's like a fly compared to a church, or an ant compared to an elephant!"

One could have sworn that he had been there himself and had seen everything with his own eyes. His friend stared straight at him, envying him intensely. There was only one thing that troubled him, and he did not hesitate to ask Pinneleh about it. "If Odessa is such a wonderful city and if the millionaire Ephrati is your relative, why have you kept so quiet about it? Why didn't you go there sooner?" Pinneleh replied to this question without a moment's hesitation.

"Dumbbell, if I said *relative,* it doesn't mean he's got to be a close relative—an uncle, or a cousin, or something. He's a distant relative, not even a third cousin. Both Ephrati and my mother come from the same town, Mezhirechka. That is, my mother's mother comes from Mezhirechka. . . ."

Pinneleh's reply may not have satisfied Sholom, but time was passing, and the two friends were so engrossed in their conversation about Odessa and Ephrati's origins that they hardly realized the morning had passed. The guests had long since finished eating the *blintzes* and were in rather high spirits. Their faces were red and moist; they stood next to the wagons taking a friendly leave of Shimeleh and his family. Everyone kissed them and wished them luck. Shmuel Eli kissed harder than anyone else (biting oddly on his upper lip as if he wanted very much to laugh) and wished the travelers all sorts of joy. He earnestly begged them to send his regards to the *whole* of Odessa, including Ephrati. "Please, for heaven's sake don't forget to remember me kindly to Ephrati!" he kept insisting.

"Goodbye and God bless you, you sons of Belial!" Sitting in the wagon, Shimeleh shouted merrily to the whole village. "Goodbye! Don't think badly of me, and may God help you to get out of this mudhole, too. Gidyap!"

"Gidyap!" repeated Pinneleh, standing up in the wagon, holding his hands in his pockets like a grownup and looking down at his friend Sholom with affection and pride. The wagons moved off.

And, after the wagons were gone, leaving behind a smell of horses and a cloud of dust, Shmuel Eli clutched his sides and burst out laughing as if a thousand imps were tickling the soles of his feet.

At that moment, false Shmuel Eli made an enemy,

and a particularly bitter one. He was Sholom Nahum Vevik's. He didn't in the least feel like laughing. On the contrary, he wanted to cry. First of all, he had lost a friend. Secondly, he was envious that Pinneleh was going so far away, and to such a city. Last and most important, he wanted to cry because the village of Voronko, once so dear and beautiful, had somehow become smaller—smaller and dingier and humbler— and suddenly it had lost all its charm, all its luster, and all its witchery. He felt an ache in his heart. Disappointed, disenchanted, and embittered, he went back to *cheder.*

19 Change Your Place, Change Your Luck

DEPARTURE FROM VORONKO.   HERSHEL WITH AN "S" PLAYS
HIS PARTNER A DIRTY TRICK.   GRANDMA MINDE'S SHROUD.

The author of this biography does not recall exactly how it came about, but it seemed that Shimeleh started it. Soon after he left, all of Voronko began to talk about moving to larger cities. Some thought of going to Borispol, others to Rezhishchev or Vasilkov, still others even farther away. "Change your place, change your luck," they said.

Nahum Vevik's children overheard that he also intended to leave; he wanted to go back to the metropolis of Pereyaslov, from which he had come when the children were still very small. The children guessed what was in the air from the words, "Change your place, change your luck."

In the children's imagination, Pereyaslov seemed immensely large, and it meant for them charm and mystery. "At Pereyaslov there's lots of easy money," the grownups said, and the youngsters listened without understanding much, but instinctively feeling that Pereyaslov must be a remarkable place. They were both overjoyed and sorry to leave the little village where they had spent the golden days of their childhood.

"What will happen," little Sholom wondered, "to the old synagogue after the Jews leave? Who will go to the east wall? And what will become of the hill beyond the synagogue? And the Jewish shops? And the treasure? . . . How can one leave such a fortune behind? What will become of it buried under the ground for so many years, waiting for a Jew to discover it? Will it be lost forever? Will it turn to dust?"

Despite the caution of the adults in not discussing "such things" before them, the children caught a word here and there: "Change your place, change your luck," "Times have changed," "Impossible to make a living," "Money is scarce. . . ."

How does changing your place change your luck? What is this thing called "a living" and how does one "make" it? The children were puzzled. But from the expressions on the faces of their elders, they surmised something was wrong. . . . Always calm, silent, and melancholy, Nahum Vevik's had become even more silent and morose. Always stooped, he had become even more bent. On his high, broad forehead, the wrinkles had doubled and deepened. He would often retire to his room with his younger brother Nissel, and they would both smoke one cigarette after another and confer for hours at a time.

During the final winter in Voronko, the Rabinowitzes had ceased to usher Queen Sabbath out with the entire community. They still celebrated the last holidays of the Rejoicing of the Law; Uncle Nissel still exchanged caps with the sheriff and danced with him artistically on the rooftop, but the dancing and the celebration were not the same as before. Even Auntie Hodel calmed down and lost much of her venom. Somehow, the whole family seemed unsettled. Only Grandma Minde remained as proud as an oak, as neat and tidy as ever. But the Sabbath treat did not seem quite the same; the apples were more wrinkled and yellow than usual and perhaps even a little spoiled; the nuts were hollow, and worms infested the figs. Grandma Minde still prayed as energetically as ever and as loudly, like a man, reading out of her large, well-used prayer book, and she still talked intimately with the Lord. But somehow the prayers and the chats were different. Something was happening to the family, something was brewing. . . .

So it went on that winter until the truth was suddenly known, and the whole village was in on the secret. Nahum Vevik's had a partner in his business; he

was a stout Jew with a red nose, whose name was
Hershel. Because he had a lisp, everyone called him
"Hershel with an 's.'" And Hershel had accomplished
his partner's ruin; plainly speaking, he had robbed
and cheated him out of the business. The village was
agog.

"For heaven's sake, Reb Nahum, why are you keeping quiet? You should insist on arbitration, take him
to the rabbi!" But when the case was brought to arbitration, the rabbi presiding, Hershel with an "s" simply laughed in their faces and spoke so coarsely (and
with an "s" in the bargain) that I am ashamed to repeat what he said.

"What can one expect of a boor?" Uncle Nissel said
over and over again, gesticulating wildly as he puffed
an exceptionally fat cigarette. He swore he would see
that thief in jail or his name wasn't Nissel; that cheat,
that boor with an "s," would go up the river for twenty-
five years at least.

"What jail? What river?" his elder brother Nahum
wanted to know, smiling bitterly and also puffing a fat
cigarette. "He played a dirty trick on me. We now
have to return to Pereyaslov, and that's it. Change
your place, change your luck."

These words were plain enough for even the youngsters to understand. But one thing was beyond their
comprehension: what sort of "trick" had Hershel
played? They had too much respect for Father to dare
ask, "Papa, what trick did he play on you?" Father,
they saw, was gradually wasting away, and every sigh,
every groan tore at their hearts.

"You will remain here for the summer so as to continue your studies. It would be a sin to take you away in the middle of the term. But during the holidays, God willing, we shall send for you."

Nahum Vevik's announced this to his children one summer's day when two wagons drove up to the house —wagons just like those that had come to take Shimeleh away. They started packing for the journey; they began their farewells to the villagers. But this was not at all like Shimeleh's leaving; there was nothing merry about the packing and leave-taking, nor was there a party. Everyone seemed in mourning; every face was sad. The entire village sympathized with the Rabinowitzes. "What a shame! May God help them! Well, change your place and change your luck!" Who was all this pity for, the children wondered. Perhaps for Grandma Minde, who had to pack her things and, in her old age, prepare for a journey.

The youngsters managed to peek into Grandma's trunk to see what was there. There were neatly ironed silk kerchiefs folded among the leaves of prayer books, silken holiday clothes and old-fashioned velvet capes with short sleeves and little squirrel tails, and, hidden away in a far corner, a pile of white linen. This was the old woman's shroud. It had been lying there, ready from time immemorial against the day—even should that be "in a hundred and twenty years." It was there so that she would not need to call upon her children for assistance. . . . Everyone knew of this, but the children were sufficiently cold-blooded to inquire, "What do you want with such a lot of white material?"

This question was put to her by the one who was the smallest in height and the largest in mischief—the author of these memoirs. He received in return a long lecture and a promise that his father would hear of this. She was not unaware that he mimicked her behind her back when she was praying—which was indeed the truth. Everything would be told, absolutely everything; she would relieve her heart once and for all.

But in the end, Grandma did not make good her threat. And when the moment came to say goodbye, she kissed each child in turn, as only a mother can, and wept, as only a mother can weep. And, when she had climbed into the wagon and the journey had begun, she called to the children, "Goodbye, children! God grant that you all live to attend my funeral!"

What a farewell!

20   *Everyone Is Crawling Away*

SHMUEL ELI PLAYS CHESS.   VILLAGERS COME TO SAY GOOD-
BYE.   ONE HAS TO BE MADE OF IRON NOT TO LAUGH.

For the villagers the day of Nahum Vevik's departure was one of mourning, but for the children it was a holiday. First, there was no school, for who could think of going to *cheder* at such a moment? And it was such wonderful fun! There were the preparations, the packing, the moving of the cupboards, the sound of clinking knives and the clinking of forks, the wagons driving up. . . . They ate in haste, as one did before Passover. But what of the money the children were to receive? For the present, the money was not in view. People were still coming to bid Nahum farewell. That is, they came to hear him say, "Stay in peace!" to which they replied, "Go in peace!" and wished the travelers a host of good things: health, happiness, all kinds of good luck. . . .

Shmuel Eli, the rabbi and cantor, was the first to arrive. He was a frequent guest at the Rabinowitzes; in fact, he came every blessed day. Just as a pious Jew will not skip a single prayer, Shmuel Eli would not skip a single game of chess with Reb Nahum. Playing chess was his greatest pleasure, winning a game from Reb Nahum the height of happiness. When he lost, he had a curious habit of shouting, and when he won, he shouted also. But he lost more often than he won. And when he lost, it was because he had made a mistake; if he had not moved such-and-such a pawn, if he had moved such-and-such a pawn, it would have been different.

Whenever Uncle Nissel was present at a game, he found Shmuel Eli's behavior unbearable. He would ask Shmuel Eli, "What are you shouting about?" Nahum, however, had a different temperament; he listened calmly to Shmuel Eli's ravings, quietly smiling into his beard as he played on. On this occasion Haya Esther was beside herself. "How can they play chess at such a time? One hour before leaving!"

"This is the last time, Haya Esther, may God bless you! You are leaving, everyone is leaving. There's no one left to play chess with!" Shmuel Eli pleaded. He pushed his hat back on his head, sat down to the game once more, seething as always, while Nahum continued to smile.

And yet the game did not proceed as smoothly as usual. Every other minute someone arrived to say goodbye. How could one be rude to a neighbor like Reb Isaac? One had to interrupt the game. True, Reb Isaac wore a goatee and prayed in a falsetto, but one could not forget that he was a disciple of the Tzadik of Lubavich, and a very pious Jew in his own right. Soon after him came Dan. Dan was a young man with white hair; his hair was as light as flax. He was a taciturn man and did not usually talk to anybody. But now that Reb Nahum was leaving Voronko, he suddenly became loquacious. He said that he too would move, if he knew where to go. He'd gladly sell his business if anybody would buy it. . . . Shmuel Eli looked angrily at him, but Dan calmly continued chattering. It appeared that Dan had always had a tongue in his head, though nobody had suspected it! He stopped talking only when other people arrived to bid farewell. All the villagers came in turn—first the men, then the women. They all wore long faces, all were morose, some with eyes red from weeping. One dear woman brought candy for the children!

The reddest eyes of all belonged to the two women who had been married in the Rabinowitz home—Fruma the One-Eyed Maid and Feigeleh the Witch, both of them dabbing their eyes and wiping their noses and making such funny faces that Sholom could not restrain himself. He just had to imitate them there and then, grimacing and wiping his nose just as they did. And the other children couldn't help but laugh, and so the fun began. "What's all this laughter about?" Mother Haya Esther demanded. She was a naturally stern woman and was now particularly flustered and excited by the impending departure. She left her work and poured out her overburdened heart on the children. All she wanted to know was the meaning of it—what was all the laughter about? Why the happiness? Fruma the Maid came to her assistance by declaring that she could swear by the Scroll of the Law that it had all been started by that little brat, that worthless, rascal, no-good. . . . The object of these fine names stood by, innocently. It is quite likely that Mother would have given him a proper farewell if Grandma Minde had not interfered. Noticing how warm it was getting for her grandson, she turned to the guests.

"Children, we have an old custom—before we say farewell, we must all sit quietly for a few minutes. . . ."

Grandma Minde sat on a disinherited couch which had been too old either to take along or to sell, and everyone followed her example. For a few moments, it was deathly still, and then came the finale, the most difficult part of all—the embraces and the leave-taking. Thank heavens, that was soon over! The wagons were ready. Once again, there was heard "Go in peace!" and once again, "Stay in peace!" Eyes were dried, noses were wiped, and the faces, oh, the faces!

How could one not mimic the women's grimaces, their trembling chins, and their blinking eyes! They did not permit one to say goodbye in a decent fashion!

But suddenly one's heart felt heavy. You felt sorry for Father, for Mother, for Grandma Minde. There they were carrying Grandma's old wrought-iron trunk, and in it lay her shroud. . . . There was a stab at the heart, one's spirit ached. One felt like crying—particularly when one saw a man like Uncle Nissel wiping his eyes surreptitiously. Was it possible for Uncle Nissel to cry? . . . Father summoned the children, one by one, and gave each of them a silver coin. Mother did the same. Earlier in the day, Grandma Minde had prepared some small change, folded in little pieces of paper. If you added it all up, it would come to quite a sum! We prayed the wagons would soon start! . . . Now they've started! The wheels begin to turn. Everyone makes a sudden move forward. "Go in peace! Best of luck!" Grandma Minde peers out of the wagon as if to take a last look at the place which she is leaving forever. . . . For a moment sorrow conquers, pity awakens—but for a moment only. Then they are extinguished. One wants to count one's newly acquired fortune. . . .

After the noise and the tumult were over, peace and quiet began. The wagons were gone, having left behind them thick clouds of dust, a smell of tar, and a strange sense of emptiness. One after another, everyone began to leave, silent and dejected, as if forsaken. Uncle Nissel disappeared almost immediately. The last to go was Shmuel Eli, the cantor. He stood looking after the departing wagons for a long time, shading his eyes from the sun although it was not shining very brightly. Then with a bitter smile he murmured to himself, "They're all crawling away like worms," and he spat.

21   Gergeleh the Thief

THE RITUAL SLAUGHTERER, A SAINTLY MAN.   GERGELEH OF
THE HARELIP.   THE ART OF STEALING APPLES.   THE
THIEF IS CAUGHT RED-HANDED.   THE TEACHER'S DEATH.

It must be made clear that the youngsters were not left uncared for in the village. Father exerted himself to find a man who would be both teacher and guardian, with whom the children could board and study, and who would keep stern watch over them. The teacher, counselor, and guardian whom he found proved eminently suitable. He was Moshe, the ritual slaughterer, son of the old Voronko slaughterer.

He was a young man with a temper of silk, an exceptionally gentle nature. He was also well versed in the Bible and the Talmud. His only defects were sickliness and an excess of good nature. He employed a new method on his pupils; it involved no rods, only soft, warm words—something to which the children were not accustomed. Because of this, they took advantage of him in every possible way and, in fact, led him around by the nose. They neither prayed nor studied, and after Moshe became seriously ill with consumption and took to his bed, they began to wander aimlessly about. So it was that they struck up an acquaintance with Gergeleh the Thief, a barefoot orphan with roguish eyes and a harelip.

Gergeleh's real name was Gershon, but, as he informed the children, his mother, the cook Sara Feiga, affectionately called him Gergeleh. The nickname "thief" was bestowed on him by his stepfather, Yosef Meyer the Woodcutter, although (as Gergeleh claimed) when the name was given him he had not yet stolen a thing. Perhaps if he had not been given such a nickname, he would never have become a thief. Now, he said, he was a thief out of spite—if only there were anything worth stealing!

This is how Gergeleh boasted to Sholom Nahum Vevik's in all seriousness and with a sophisticated air. Sholom was delighted with this clever, harelipped boy. Their friendship started in Moshe's schoolroom. Throughout most of the week, Moshe was a teacher, but on Thursdays he became a ritual slaughterer, and all the women and girls assembled in the *heder* with their chickens, ducks, and geese. Among them, one could always find a little urchin with a harelip; this was Gergeleh, who would also be carrying a chicken which his mother, the cook, had sent to be slaughtered for Sabbath. Sitting among the women, waiting for Moshe, Gergeleh amused the audience by making such comical grimaces that all the women showered him with goodnatured invective: "thief," "apostate," "plague"— at the same time laughing themselves sick at him. "That's a boy after my own heart," Sholom Nahum Vevik's thought, and straightway became friends with Gergeleh. This friendship, naturally, had to be conducted in secret, because any *decent* boy would have got a good scolding for associating with a cook's son—and a thief besides.

There was, however, a certain charm in associating with a boy whom one could meet only at twilight and with whom one could only exchange a few words. There was a peculiar pleasure in slipping a penny, a candy, or sometimes even an ordinary piece of bread into his hand when no one was looking. Gergeleh accepted everything with delight—but not as charity. He didn't even thank you. He received whatever you gave as if it were his due; he would even order you to bring more the next day and instruct you how to "get" it—or, more bluntly, how to steal it for him. "Getting" things must not be done crudely—it must be done artistically. In this fashion he taught his comrades —and in a surprisingly short time, too—how to "get" apples and pears at the market, free of charge. This was not the same as stealing from an orchard, for what decent boy would dare climb a fence, like a common peasant, jump into a strange orchard where there might be a watchman who could break his bones or a dog on a chain that could tear him to bits? . . . Gergeleh taught one how to get as many apples as one's heart desired without breaking the commandment "Thou shalt not steal." You will hear how this was done and judge for yourself whether it could possibly be called stealing.

Summertime. The apples and pears have just appeared. It is already evening. The women are still sitting about with their wares spread out on little stalls or on the ground. They are chatting about this year's fruit harvest. They remark that there has been no rain, and when there is no rain there is a great deal of dust, and when there is dust there are many flies. . . . Their husbands are in the synagogue, hurrying through the evening prayer. This is the right moment. It is the time to start working for free apples. The young rascals are all barefoot, armed with sticks tipped by hooked nails. They begin to run. This is called "the post chaise." One boy is the horse, the others the passengers who hold him by the reins and spur him on. They whistle and yell "Gee up!" Just as they reach a pile of apples, Gergeleh gives a command, . "Down sticks!" and all the boys strike the pile with their nailed sticks. Since they have raised a cloud of dust by running, no one notices that several apples have rolled off. The rogues run a little farther, and Gergeleh, with the rest of the gang, lies on the ground and collects the booty. They stuff the apples into their pockets or cram them into their mouths. This is living! Actually, stealing isn't so particularly wonderful, nor the apples exceptionally good either—but the point is, it's a great game!

Gergeleh was on the whole a merry youngster, playful and laughter-loving, although he had never experienced any kindness and every God-fearing individual thought it necessary to chastize him. He was a poor boy, and an orphan besides. Who was there to defend him? Moreover, everyone knew he was a thief. Melach, the beadle of the synagogue, caught him once with a stolen prayer book. Ruda Batia, who baked rolls and cakes, once pulled half a doughnut out of his shirt. It was an act of virtue to punish such a scoundrel. And he had a wicked tongue. He knew everyone's weak spot, had a nickname for everyone, and, since he had nothing to lose, liked to thrust his leg in one's path like a poker, to make one trip and stretch out full length—even the rabbi himself, or the rabbi's wife, or the slaughterer's wife. They'd go "bang" on the ground. . . . This trick titillated little Sholom's fancy, and in due course he came to love Gergeleh sufficiently to steal for him large slices of bread from the slaughterer's wife, and sometimes even a piece of sugar from the sugarbowl. Gergeleh loved sugar. However, more than anything else, he loved to smoke; he would languish for a cigarette. But where could you get a cigarette when the teacher was sick and never smoked, and Father was away? So Gergeleh advised Sholom to visit Uncle Nissel more often—Uncle Nissel smoked wonderful tobacco.

This was excellent counsel. Uncle Nissel was a generous soul; the tobacco box stood open, free for everyone, on the mantelpiece under the mirror. Little Sholom began to frequent Uncle Nissel's home. He would stick his fist into the box, clutch a handful of tobacco, and spill it into his trouser pocket. Of course, it had to be Auntie Hodel who caught him at it! And with that the heavens crashed to earth—it was the end of the world! There was no punishment that the little culprit did not deserve. He himself admitted that the worse the punishment, the better. And, head bent low, he awaited the consequences.

But it was not he who was punished; it was Uncle Nissel. Auntie Hodel's mouth opened wide, and she commenced to give him a piece of her mind. "Small wonder," she said, "when the child comes from a family of thieves!" Uncle Nissel listened to her with a dour expression, and then took his nephew aside and commanded him to tell the truth: for whom did he steal the tobacco? He had noticed for some time that someone was taking his tobacco, but he had kept still about it. Now he wanted the whole truth. He took the boy between his knees, patted his cheek, and told him gently that he had to make a choice: either he must name the man for whom he was stealing, or else he, Uncle Nissel, would immediately write his brother Nahum and inform him that one of his sons was a thief. The little culprit listened to his uncle, feeling his heart being torn to pieces. He pictured his father's somber face and heard his sighs—he was ready to confess. But then he recalled his secret friend, his beloved Gergeleh the Thief, and all the punishment he would suffer if his identity was revealed. The whole village would rise up against Gergeleh. They'd whip him; they'd strip him naked and pillory him. Perhaps they would even lead him through the streets so that everyone could cry, "Shame!". . . No, he couldn't betray him. He had no alternative but to lie and insist that he alone was to blame; he took the tobacco for himself; he liked to smoke.

Uncle Nissel, however, was not satisfied, and he decided to test the boy. He took a large cigarette, lit it, and put it between the boy's lips. He commanded him, in front of the whole family, to take a deep puff.

There was no escape. Sholom stood trial as best he could. He bravely inhaled the smoke and even tried to blow it through his nose, like a man. But it was too much. He began to cough so violently that everyone was frightened and began to throw water in his face and bang him on his back. In the excitement, the theft was almost forgotten. Moreover, a miracle took place. Actually, it wasn't really a miracle—it was a misfortune! Some people arrived to take Uncle Nissel to Moshe the Slaughterer. Moshe was dying.

Here was a more severe blow for the young culprit. The children had never had a teacher whom they loved so well. Moshe was more angel than teacher. Only now, when the pallbearers lifted his body to their shoulders and carried it shrouded in black to the cemetery, with the whole village following, did Nahum Vevik's children realize what a treasure they had lost and what a trial they had been to him. And rivers of tears flowed from their eyes.

Sholom wept more bitterly than anyone, and he wept

longest. He had been, he felt, the worst transgressor, the most hardened sinner. Moshe had always considered him his best and most truthful pupil; yet he had seldom known his Thursday lesson. He had only pretended he had known it; he had swayed, sung, mumbled, and gesticulated—he had deceived him, yes, deceived, *deceived* him! How often had he skipped more than half the prayer? How often had he omitted the evening prayer altogether and, instead, chased around with Gergeleh the Thief, teasing the priest's dogs, stealing apples from the marketplace? . . . Here, in this world, the teacher had known nothing of this; if he had been told, he would not have believed it. But there, in the other world, he knew everything, everything. . . .

22 *Meyer Velvel the Coachman and his Steeds*

UNCLE NISSEL, A SCAMP AMONG SCAMPS. MEYER VELVEL'S WAGON AND THE THREE STEEDS, WISER, DANCER, AND NOBLE. THE COACHMAN TELLS THE STORY OF HIS LIFE.

It was the end of the summer and still quite warm, although the smell of the month of Elul was already in the air. A wagon harnessed to three horses came from the great city of Pereyaslov and drove up to Uncle

Nissel's house. The coachman, a garrulous Jew called Meyer Velvel, ungirdled himself and from an unseen pocket extracted a letter written by Nahum Vevik's to his brother Nissel Rabinowitz. Nahum wrote that he was sending a wagon with horses for the children, also three pairs of shoes and some food—buns, hard-boiled eggs, and pears, which ought to suffice for a two days' journey. In addition, Grandma Minde was sending a warm blanket and an old shawl to keep them warm in case of cold or rain. The coachman was instructed to depart with the children on the very next morning, right after prayers, and to spend the night in Borispol, so that they should arrive in Pereyaslov on the evening of the following day.

There are no words adequate to describe the joy of Nahum Vevik's children when they were informed of the contents of the letter and the three pairs of shoes. They did not know what was more wonderful, the new shoes, the prospect of two whole days in a wagon with three horses, or the fact that on the evening of the second day they would already be in the big city of Pereyaslov!

"Come here, rascals! Sit down and try on the shoes!" commanded Uncle Nissel, giving each one a slap, some on the nose and some on the ear.

Uncle Nissel loved children, whether his own or another's. To receive a slap from him was a pleasure, and not a punishment, even if it stung for half an hour afterward. A slap from a loved one is a caress.

The children loved their uncle because he never punished them, never lectured them and, unlike the others, never kept a strict eye on their studies and prayers. In fact, among rascals he was a rascal himself. He enjoyed a good laugh and a clever joke. He found it amusing to hold snuff under the nose of some old Jew who had dozed off in the synagogue, and then to wish him "God bless you!" when he woke coughing and sneezing. On *Simchath Torah,* he was more mischievous than anyone. It was he who got the drunkard, Gedalia, drunk on brandy and helped the children bind him like a sheep, hand and foot, and lock him up in a shed, his hands tied with a long rope to a log of wood with a bell attached. When Gedalia sobered up, he rose and started the bell ringing, and the whole village came on the run, asking "Where's the fire?"

This should make it quite clear how difficult it was to part from such an uncle. During the leave-taking, he consoled the children with kind words and cheerful slaps on the back. "Never mind, never mind, we'll meet again! I shan't remain long here either." It was as he said, as the reader already knows.

The children felt taller in their new shoes; they felt wonderfully happy as they explored the wagon and made the acquaintance of the three horses and the coachman, who were taking them to the big city.

The wagon was a wagon like any other, adorned with a gray patched canopy, and with its floor carpeted with hay which in turn was covered with a mat. It was soft and pleasant to sit on. The children learned the full implications of this on the second day, when it seemed that not a single bone in their bodies was whole and sound. Each of the three horses deserves individual attention, because each of the three "steeds," as Meyer Velvel called them, was as different from the others as chalk is from cheese.

It was a Jewish team, and we will begin with the middle horse, the wheeler. The name Meyer Velvel had given it was "Wiser." Why "Wiser," no one could discover. Perhaps "Wiser" came from "wise." As a matter of fact, this "steed" was not overburdened with wisdom, although he was heavily burdened with years, a fact which was obvious from his old muzzle, narrow eyes, bald tail, and the sharp bones that stuck out of a back that had once been broad. And yet, despite his age, the whole weight of the wagon was practically on him alone because the two other "steeds," his partners on the flank, only pretended to pull.

The other two also had names. One was called "Dancer" because of his dancing gait—and he did nothing but dance. All of his four legs danced, and each one danced separately; apparently they did not agree among themselves, and therefore no good came of all this dancing. He only interfered with Wiser. Even worse, he caused the wagon to jolt until one's insides were very nearly shaken out. But Meyer Velvel had his revenge on him. "I'll make you dance!" he would say, lashing him with the whip or the whip handle! And to teach him sense he whipped him the whole journey. But it didn't help at all. Dancer did not move an eyelash, and he did not stop dancing. In fact, he only behaved worse; he replied by rearing, as if to say, "Well, you've asked for it!" A short horse, much smaller than Wiser, his face, however, was shrewder. Perhaps Meyer

Velvel was not exaggerating when he boasted that Dancer had once been a "remarkable steed." But, he said, ever since a spell had been cast on his legs, no one could manage him. Ever since Dancer had fallen into his hands, Meyer Velvel had been teaching him sense.

His third "steed" Meyer Velvel left in peace. Only occasionally would he give her a light swish with the whip, and this, as it were, for the sake of propriety. She was a small, fat mare with shaggy legs. Meyer Velvel called her "Noble" since she came from a noble family—she had belonged to a priest, he told the children. And how did she get to Meyer Velvel? This was a long story which cannot possibly be reconstructed. To begin with, it happened so long ago that I cannot possibly recall all the details. Secondly, even in those days Meyer Velvel's yarn did not hang together. All he remembered was that Noble was (and he said it with a smile) stolen. That is, it wasn't he (God forbid!) who did the stealing—it was the work of others. All he did was buy her cheaply from the thieves, never suspecting (not him, may he be as free of poverty and misfortune as he was of guilt in this instance!) that the horse had been stolen. If he had known she had been stolen—and stolen from a priest—he would have had nothing to do with her, not even if you paid him. No sir, not even if you had actually paid him to take her! It wasn't because he was a saint or a hypocrite. What business was it of his if someone else were a thief? He wouldn't be whipped for the sins of others in the next world. But there was another reason why. He did not want to have any "connections" with the police. That was because he had once had a bit of bad luck; he had been slandered; colleagues of his, enemies, had played a nasty trick on him. All because of Yankel Bulgach, a plague upon his head. . . .

And this is where Meyer Velvel began another story, which was followed with another, and after this still another. After hearing all his stories, one could well believe that Meyer Velvel had once had very close "connections" with the police.

Meyer Velvel had one outstanding virtue; he was, as we have seen, extremely talkative, and his chatter entertained his young passengers the entire journey from Voronko to Borispol, and from Borispol to Pereyaslov. Not for one instant did he shut his mouth. The children learned all there was to know about him: how, as a boy, he had served as a driver for Yankel Bulgach; how he had afterward married and become a coachman on his own; and how Yankel Bulgach had worried and hounded him. But Meyer Velvel didn't scare, not he! . . . He also told about his wife, who had been very pretty in her youth, a lovely creature, and how he had pined away for her, because of her beauty, till he had almost expired. If he were single today, he wouldn't even look at her twice, but in those days he had been a mere babe in arms. . . .

After he had finished telling his history, Meyer Velvel returned to the story of Yankel Bulgach and the other coachmen. He called each one by his correct name, recounted how many and what kind of horses each one owned, who had real "steeds," and who had "jades," "carcasses," and "monstrosities."

From coachmen, Meyer Velvel went on to horse deal-
ers, gypsies, horse thieves, and "fingerers." He made the
children understand that the difference between a thief
and a "fingerer" was that the former stole the horse, and
the latter discovered its hiding place. One therefore had
to be on even better terms with the "fingerers" than
with the thieves. . . . Surely, the children would never
have learned as much in two years as they did during
their two days' journey with Meyer Velvel.

Now that we are already acquainted with the coachman, his wagon, and his three "steeds," we can return
briefly to Voronko in order to describe how the hero
of this biography took leave of his village before departing forever.

23   Voronko, Farewell!

THE HERO TAKES LEAVE OF HIS VILLAGE AND THE TREASURE.
A STUPID INCIDENT WITH FRUMA THE MAID.   HE PRESENTS
GERGELEH WITH A GIFT.

They may have become disillusioned with their village;
they may have wearied of the villagers; Pinneleh
Shimeleh's may have belittled Voronko—and yet, before
the departure of Nahum Vevik's children for the big
city, Voronko's charm revived, its former luster returned, and they found it painful to leave.

Sholom Nahum Vevik's took leave of the village as of a human being, a beloved, faithful friend. He began his farewells with the yard and the garden, and he did not forget a single tree—all this now belonged to others. He ended with the hill beyond the synagogue and the meadow outside the village where he had spent so many hours with his closest friends, the first of whom had been Shmulik the Orphan, and the last of whom had been Gergeleh the Thief.

He felt the greatest emotion when he reached the place where, according to Shmulik, the treasure lay hidden. He stood there alone, bewitched by the mysterious silence as a thousand thoughts passed through his mind: What would become of the treasure if a Gentile should find it instead of a Jew? . . . Was it possible for a Gentile to find it? . . . Only one person knew the answers—Shmulik. And where was Shmulik now? . . . Would they ever meet again? What would happen if they should meet? They would certainly return to Voronko so as to revisit the old places where they had spent the best of their childhood. Then they would begin the task of discovering the treasure. First one of them would fast, and then the other, and, when they had finished fasting and reading the Psalms, they would begin their search. And when they had found the treasure, they would divide it into two equal parts, half for each—and then, what a holiday they would have! The largest portion of Sholom's share would, of course, go to Father. Uncle Nissel would get a nice hunk, too, and so would Uncle Pinney, not to mention the other relatives. But he would leave a whole lot of the treasure in the

village, for the Jews of Voronko. Moshe the Slaughterer's widow must have enough to stop her talk of re-
marrying and prevent her traipsing off to Fastov to her
poor relatives who could scarcely make ends meet
themselves. . . . Fruma the Maid and Feigeleh the
Witch, the two almoners, would collect more than their
husbands had ever dreamed of, even though they did
not deserve it. . . . Old Ruda Batia, who baked cakes
and buns and supported an entire family, would appreciate a little rest for her swollen hands in her old age.
. . . And why should Melach the Beadle and the
drunkard Gedalia be overlooked? . . . Or Shmuel Eli,
who was forever complaining that Voronko was no
place for him, that he had a fine voice and would out-
sing the greatest cantor if he only were given music—
well, the music would be supplied. . . .

There only remained Gergeleh the Thief. What could
be done to keep him from stealing? Well, his mother
must stop working as a cook. Next, his stepfather, the
woodcutter, must be bought a house and his pockets
filled with money. But it had to be made clear to him
that this was not being done for his sake, but for his
stepson, Gergeleh, so that he would stop beating him
and calling him a thief. . . .

Just then, Gergeleh the Thief appeared in person,
barefoot as usual and dressed in tatters.

"Where did you come from?"

"Where did *you* come from?"

They began to walk together, and as they walked
they spoke. Sholom informed Gergeleh that he was going away, but Gergeleh knew all about it already. He

had heard the news and had even seen the wagon with the three horses.

"Oh, so you saw them? Well, what do you think of them?"

"Think of what?"

"The horses."

"What should I think? Just horses. . . ."

"Well, how did you like the wagon?"

"Just a wagon. . . ."

It was clear that Gergeleh was in a bad humor, and his friend sought to cheer him up.

"Do you know, I was just thinking about you when you came?"

"Honest? What were you thinking?"

"I was thinking . . . well, it had to do with you and the treasure. . . ."

"What treasure?"

Sholom felt uncomfortable. Should he tell? Gergeleh asked again, "What treasure?" There was no way out—he had to tell him. Becoming interested, Gergeleh wanted to know, "Just where is this treasure?" Sholom became even more uncomfortable. Should he tell, or shouldn't he? Gergeleh's eyes lit up. "Why are you so afraid? Are you scared I'll grab it?" Now Sholom was sorry he had begun the conversation, and when he replied he did so in the supercilious tone Shmulik had once used to him.

"Dumbbell, even if I told you where it was, that wouldn't be much use to you; you've got to know the Kabbala, and you've got to fast forty days, and on the forty-first day. . . ."

"On the forty-first day you'll turn into a *shlemiel!*"
Gergeleh interrupted, and he glanced at his friend's
new shoes. They seemed to fascinate him.

"New?"

Sholom suddenly felt terribly ashamed that he was
wearing brand-new shoes. Here was Gergeleh barefoot.
He blurted out, "Come with me to Uncle Nissel's and
I'll give you something. . . ."

"Sure!" Gergeleh seemed pleased, and the two of
them walked quickly off. At Uncle Nissel's, they found a
host of friends and acquaintances come to send regards
to Father and Mother and to say goodbye.

In the crowd were the two almoners, Fruma the Maid
and Feigeleh the Witch, for the time being without their
husbands, who were due later. Everyone looked respectfully at the children who were going to the big
city. Their manner had altered; they gave advice on
how to travel, on where to stop in Borispol. . . . Uncle
Nissel poked them as usual and asked the rascals if they
intended to write to him. A foolish question! Why, they
would write every week; no, twice a week; no, every
single day! . . . As for Shmuel Eli, he had a special
greeting for Father. He wanted Reb Nahum to know
that, ever since he had left the village, he, Shmuel Eli,
had not played even a single game of chess—Voronko
was a wilderness!

Auntie Hodel had suddenly become soft as silk and
sweet as sugar. She could not understand how children
could be sent hungry on a journey! What sort of food
were rolls, and hard-boiled eggs and pears, and for a
two days' trip! The children would die of starvation!

She packed as much food as she could: a small pot of goosefat, a jar of saccharine jelly (apparently left over from the summer before), and plum jam that turned out to be as sour as vinegar.

While Auntie Hodel was packing and the children were busy saying goodbye, an unpleasant incident occurred between Fruma the Maid and Gergeleh the Thief. No sooner had Fruma spied the boy than she squinted at him with her bad eye and asked Feigeleh, "What is that crook doing here?" Gergeleh did not wait for the answer. He had his own question. Said he, "What's that blind horror doing here?" If Sholom had not taken his friend by the hand and led him out into the yard, there might have been a dreadful scene. (On such a special occasion, anything was permissible—even associating with Gergeleh the Thief.)

"I said I'd give you something. . . . Here!"

And, very pleased with his own magnanimity, Sholom Nahum Vevik's flourished a pair of old shoes which he pulled out from under his coat skirts. Apparently Gergeleh had counted on a different kind of gift—certainly not a pair of old shoes. Also, he had just been through the incident with one-eyed Fruma, and before that he had been annoyed that his friend had kept secret the treasure's hiding place. And, anyway, he was out of sorts that day. He took the shoes from Sholom and threw them down in anger. Still barefoot, he ran from the yard and disappeared.

A stupid incident, yet how much sorrow it caused! It marred the departure; it robbed his first, great, wonderful journey of its sweetness. No matter how hard Sholom tried to drive from his mind the melancholy picture of his offended friend, nevertheless it returned, and guilt gnawed at his heart: "See what you've done; you've offended a friend!"

And so they drove away from the marketplace, past the shops, past the houses, past the cemetery, past the peasants' graves; they drove over the bridge and left the meadow behind them. Goodbye, Voronko!

Sholom felt a peculiar contraction in his throat. Pity for the tiny village swept over him. It seemed to him as if this place had suffered a loss. This feeling, along with his feeling of regret about Gergeleh, made him melt into tears. He turned his head aside, so that his brothers should not see, wiped away the tears, and for the last time softly bade the little village goodbye.

"Farewell, Voronko, farewell!"

24 *The Journey*

Only those who have been raised in a small village and
have left it, never having been away before, can appreciate the happy state of mind of the youngsters on
their first wonderful journey. At first, they could not
settle themselves comfortably in the wagon. They tried
reclining, as Father did on Passover Eve when he lay on
his cushioned couch during the *Seder.* They stuck their
hands in their pockets and stretched out full length, or
they stood up and held on to the hoops of the canopy.
This last practice, however, was forbidden by Meyer
Velvel. The fact that he and the children had become
great friends, and that he had told them his whole
repertory of stories, did not prevent him from promising
them that if they injured his wagon, he would tear them
limb from limb. This said, Meyer Velvel lashed his
"steeds" and drove on.

Whoever recalls his first journey knows how the road
flies past and how the ground disappears from beneath
the wheels and the horses' hooves. He also knows how
the fresh air flows into one's nostrils and throat and how
delightfully it tickles. He knows the smell of autumn

grass and has seen the tardy leaf on a solitary tree. It is all so exhilarating one wants to sing. One feels endlessly and eternally good.

And, after leaving the houses and the little bridge and the meadow and the cemetery, one speeds on and on until one sees giants motioning with huge arms. Up and down, up and down they go. One is terrified until, on approaching them, one realizes they are only windmills. Soon they also disappear. Then there is nothing but sky and field, field and sky. It would be fun to jump out of the wagon; it would be even more fun to fly out, to swim upward into that measureless blue, a blue without beginning or end. One cannot help but think of the insignificance of man and of the greatness of Him who created this beautiful world. Lulled by such meditations, one begins to nod.

Suddenly, through the dream, a large cart hitched to a pair of enormous oxen with tremendous horns burst into view. Beside it walked a barefoot peasant in a large hat. Meyer Velvel greeted him in a mixture of Yiddish and Russian, "Greetings, son of man, may the heavens keep your pants from falling down!" The peasant wasn't sure whether the Jew was saying something good or something bad. For a moment he stood perplexed, and then with a shake of his head he mumbled, "Thank you" through his nose and continued on his way. The youngsters burst out laughing. Meyer Velvel did not even smile. He turned his head and asked, "What is so funny?" The old fraud! And that was how it went the first day of that happy journey at the summer's end.

The last days of summer—how lovely they were! The

fields were bare; in places they had been ploughed under; the corn already had been removed; here and there a blade of grass, a spike, or a flower still peeped out. In the peasants' vegetable patches, unripe watermelons still lay on the ground next to long squashes. Tall sunflowers, standing straight and proud, flaunted their rich yellow caps. The air was still full of flies, and little bugs hummed and buzzed; grasshoppers hopped aimlessly; butterflies and particles of dust drifted solemnly aloft. The fragrance of the fields overwhelmed you. The world around seemed so large and the sky above so boundless that it again occurred to you that human beings were small, much too small for so large a world, and that God alone, whose glory filled the universe, was equal to it.

"Get out, you rascals, here we are in Borispol! We're spending the night here. Tomorrow, God be willing, we're off again."

Borispol was a new town. Or, more properly, a new village, a rather large-sized village. There were the same small houses here as in Voronko. The people also seemed to be the same, except that their noses were different. It may have been a coincidence, but the children were astonished to note that the innkeeper, his wife, and their four grown-up daughters all had amazingly long noses. As if this were not enough, their servant had the longest nose of all! . . . Once he had learned from the coachman who the distinguished visitors were, the long-nosed innkeeper greeted them cordially. He commanded his long-nosed servant to heat the samovar, motioned for his long-nosed wife to serve refreshments, and ordered his long-nosed daughters to put on their shoes.

A few moments later and the young travelers had made friends with the barefoot girls. The latter were very inquisitive and cross-examined the boys. They wanted to know where they came from, where they were going, what their names were, how they liked Borispol. Indeed, they wanted to know everything— even how old each of them was. The boys and girls together tasted Auntie Hodel's sour plum jam, and their laughter echoed through the rooms. Then they began to play blindman's buff. The girls grew excited, and whenever they caught one of the boys they held him so tightly to them that they left him breathless.

At night, the guests slept on the hay-covered floor. Lest they consider themselves slighted, the long-nosed hostess pointed out that her daughters also slept on the floor, in another corner of the room. "And it's not hurting their growth, knock on wood!" she added, blowing her long nose. The boys would have been pleased with their novel bed had they not been too shy to undress in front of the girls. The girls, however, were not in the least shy and took their blouses off quite unselfconsciously. Barefoot, with their throats exposed, clad only in their skirts, they let down their hair, exchanging glances among themselves and making eyes at the boys, and giggling, endlessly giggling.

"Be still!" the hostess commanded, extinguishing the hanging lamps. But in the darkness, half-suppressed laughter and the rustle of hay were still heard from both sides of the room. Soon, however, that sleep which comes only to the innocent and the young brought silence.

The children were awakened by the innkeeper intoning the morning prayer, and the familiar melody told them that it was dawn, time to continue their journey to Pereyaslov. The mere thought of this filled their hearts with joy. Meyer Velvel wound up his phylacteries, and then, his face shining like a saint's, he left the room to harness the "steeds." He had an argument with Wiser, Dancer, and Noble in his own tongue; he punished each one in turn, but Dancer got the most, so that "he should learn not to dance when no music was playing!"

The sun was shining brightly and the yard seemed bathed in molten gold, and diamonds sparkled everywhere. Even the rubbish heap, which had been building through the summer (perhaps through two summers), was flooded with gold. A rooster and some hens rummaged in the heap, and they seemed to be cast out of pure gold down to the tiniest feather. Their cackles were a delight to the ear, their fussing, a joy. And when the golden rooster perched himself on top of the heap and shut his eyes and emitted a beautiful, long-drawn-out "Cock-a-doodle-do" in the manner of a born cantor, once again one sensed the beauty of the world and the greatness of the Creator. One wanted to praise Him —but not with prayers, like the innkeeper or the coachman. No, the children had not the slightest wish to pray. Prayers had long since wearied them. They wanted to praise God and thank Him in their own fashion, quietly, in the depths of their hearts.

"Get into the wagon, you rascals! We still have a whole day's traveling," Meyer Velvel said, seeking to speed them up. He paid for the hay and the straw and said goodbye to the innkeeper. The youngsters also said cordial goodbyes to the long-nosed family and climbed into the wagon.

A new freshness, a new sweetness, a new spaciousness overwhelmed them as soon as the bouncing wagon rolled out of Borispol and again emerged into the wide world of fields and gardens, sand, woods, and sky. Sky, sky, sky everywhere. . . . Now one felt there was perhaps too much of it. They became rather bored, and it was not so much the sky that bored them as the traveling and, even more than the traveling, the coachman and his endless stories. And there was a continual banging in their heads, a twitching in their eyes, and their sides began to hurt from the shaking and the jolting. Bump, bump, bump, bump! They thought the bumping would go on forever. They felt a desire to leave the wagon, a longing for firm ground, for home, for their village, for dear old Voronko. . . . The hero of this biography huddled in a corner of the wagon, sighed gently, and with all his heart and soul said goodbye over and over again, whispering softly to himself, so that his brothers should not hear:

"Farewell, Voronko, farewell, farewell. . . ."

25 In the New Home

PEREYASLOV.   THE COLD RECEPTION.   THE EMPTY INN.
THE YOUNGSTERS ARE DISAPPOINTED.   FATHER IS CAREWORN.

After two days of being shaken up and jolted, of being bumped and tossed, after two days of swallowing dust and listening to the coachman's interminable yarns, the young travelers felt they must surely be very near their new home. A few moments more and through the dark night began to appear distant lights, the first sign of a city. Then the wheels began to clatter over cobblestones, and the wagon shook harder than ever. Now they were in a real city, in the great city of Pereyaslov. Meyer Velvel's wagon clattered noisily into a dark yard. Over the door of the house hung a smoky lantern and a bundle of straw—the customary sign of an inn.

The fact that their parents' new business was keeping an inn was a surprise and a shock to the children. How could their father Nahum possibly receive paying guests? How could their mother Haya Esther cook for people? How could Grandma Minde wait on them? They could not picture a greater comedown nor worse humiliation. Sholom, the dreamer, who was forever conjuring up visions of a better place and time, who was constantly immersed in fantasies of treasures, later mourned in secret, weeping quietly, as he thought with longing of dear little Voronko. Now it was inexplicable to him that the grownups had said, "Change your place and change your luck!" A fine new place this was! Wonderful new luck!

"All right, climb out, rascals, we've arrived," Meyer Velvel announced gaily, and after a prolonged "Whoa!" drew his horses up at the entrance of the inn.

The weak, hungry youngsters climbed from the wagon one by one, and stretched their cramped limbs. Suddenly the door of the inn opened and silhouettes began to appear on the porch. In the darkness, one could make out who was there by voice and movement only. The first silhouette, tall and broad, was Grandma Minde. She stuck her old head through the doorway and exclaimed, "They're here, thank heavens!" The second silhouette was small and lively—and this was Mother. She asked someone, "Are they really here?" and a tall, thin figure replied joyously, "Yes, they're here!" This was Father, who was now called Reb Nahum Rabinowitz—no longer Nahum Vevik's. Grandfather Vevik had evidently been mustered out, now they were in the big city. . . .

The reception was not quite what the children had anticipated. Of course, they received their share of kisses—but they were cooler than they had imagined. When they were asked, "Well, how are you?" what could they reply but "All right"? The first to recollect that they might wish to eat was Grandma Minde. "Are you hungry?" Of course they were hungry! "Will you have something to eat?" They most certainly would!

"Have you said the evening prayer?" Yes, they had said it. . . .

Mother hurried into the kitchen to prepare something. In the meantime, Father inquired how their studies were going. Certainly they'd made progress! But who cared about studies just then? What they wanted to do was to take a look at their new home!

They twisted and stretched their necks in all directions, investigating this new universe into which they had fallen. They were in a large, somber, rather haphazard-looking apartment, which was composed of a number of small rooms, separated from one another by thin partitions. These were the guest rooms—but as for guests, there was not a one. . . . In the middle of the apartment was a large hall. Here the youngsters found their Voronko furniture. There was the round red table standing on three legs, the ancient red couch with its worn-out seat, the red oval mirror with the two carved hands, folded like a priest's, at the top, and the glass cupboard. From out of the cupboard peeped the Passover dishes, and there were the silver *Hanukah* candelabrum and the old silver spice holder which was fashioned like an apple perched on top of a large leafy twig. But where was the rest of the silverware? Where were the gilt goblets, the decanters, the wine glasses, the knives, the forks, and the spoons? Where had they disappeared to? Much later the children learned that all those things, along with Mother's jewelry and pearls, had been pawned; nor were they ever to be redeemed.

"Now wash your hands!" Grandma Minde said when Mother brought a rather meager meal from the kitchen.

The meal consisted of warmed-over gruel and beans. There was also some stale bread. Mother cut the bread herself and distributed a slice to each child. Nothing like this had ever happened before! Father sat apart from them, still inquiring about their progress in the Bible. He seemed satisfied; the children had really accomplished a good deal. As for Sholom, it goes without saying that so far as the Bible was concerned, he was a master. He could recite entire chapters of Isaiah by heart, rattling them off like a machine!

"All right, now it's time for bed," Mother said, removing what remained of the bread from the table and locking it up in the cupboard. This, too, had never happened in Voronko. The children felt humiliated.

Perhaps the journey had been too long and strenuous; perhaps their reception had not been hearty enough; certainly the meal had been too meager. At any rate, the new home which the children had dreamed about was not what they had expected. They had anticipated too much, and they felt cheated. They were happy when it was time to say the evening prayer and go to bed.

They slept on straw pallets, which were spread over the floor in a large, completely unfurnished room—a sort of corridor between the hall and the kitchen. Here it was very dark, and for a long time Sholom was unable to fall asleep. All sorts of thoughts buzzed in his head, all kinds of imaginings along with endless questions. Why was it so dark and somber here? Why did everyone look so worried? What had happened to Mother to make her so stingy? What had happened to Father? He was so bent, so old looking; it made your heart ache to see his yellow wrinkled face. Could it be, as they had said in Voronko, that money was scarce? Surely this could not be the "new place" nor the "new luck"! What was to be done about it? There was only one remedy—the treasure. Oh, if he could only have brought with him the tiniest part of it! But it was still hidden in Voronko.

The treasure reminded him of his friend Shmulik the Orphan. He fell asleep and dreamed about gold and silver, diamonds and precious stones. In the dream, Shmulik appeared, dear Shmulik with his charming face and glossy hair. Sholom fancied he heard the low, rather husky voice talking to him sweetly, affectionately, like an adult trying to console him, "Don't worry, dear Sholom. Here's a gift for you—it's one of the two magic stones. Choose whichever you wish, the stone called *Yashpoh* or the stone called *Kadkod*. . . ." Sholom hesitated. He had forgotten which stone was better . . . and while he was trying to make up his mind, Gergeleh the Thief jumped in, snatched both stones, and disappeared with them. Pinneleh Shimeleh's—where did *he* come from?—held his hands in his pockets and roared with laughter. "What are you laughing at, Pinneleh?" "Your Auntie Hodel and her plum jam! Ha, ha, ha!"

"Get up, lazybones! Just look, you can't wake them! The house has to be cleaned, dinner cooked—and they sleep! Sweet dreams to them!" Thus complained Mother, small energetic Haya Esther, now weary and harassed by housework which she had to do all by herself.

"*Ee . . . o . . . nu!* Prayers!" Grandma Minde came

to her aid, holding her large prayerbook, turning page after page, and reading on diligently, since a prayer must not be interrupted.

"After prayers, you'll visit your relations and get acquainted with them, and after the holidays, God willing, you'll start school," added Father more gently. Although it was still warm outside, he was dressed in an odd-looking dressing gown lined with cat's fur. He was bent and careworn, and as he puffed on a long cigarette he sighed so deeply that one's heart bled for him. Somehow he looked smaller than before, smaller and older. . . . And one wanted to leave the house as quickly as possible, run out of doors, and look at the new city and meet one's relations.

26   Aunt Hannah and her Home

HICKS IN A BIG CITY.   GETTING ACQUAINTED WITH THE RELATIVES.   AUNT HANNAH AND HER CHILDREN.   SHOLOM IS TESTED IN THE BIBLE.

If the city seemed empty and dark at night, in the morning it shone and glittered and delighted the young villagers. They were delighted by everything. Never had they seen such long broad streets, flanked by wooden sidewalks, such housetops of tin, such windows with red, green, and blue shutters, and brick shops with iron doors. The marketplace, churches, synagogues, even the people—everyone and everything seemed so big, lovely, clean, and festive! Apparently Pinneleh Shime-leh's had not exaggerated when he had described the wonders of a big city. When, with Father, they went to meet their relatives, their feet glided over wooden side-walks as though on skates. Out of respect for Father they could not stop everywhere to gaze their fill at the marvels before their eyes.

Father walked ahead, as was customary; the children straggled behind. Entering a large courtyard, they passed from a big sunny glass corridor into a princely house. Its floors were waxed; soft couches and chairs were everywhere, tall mirrors, ceiling-high carved cup-boards, glass candelabra suspended from the ceilings, and copper candlesticks on the walls. A real mansion, a palace!

This was the home of Aunt Hannah. It was a peculiar home, a home without a father. Aunt Hannah was a widow, and her children obeyed neither their mother nor their tutor. It was a small anarchy; everyone did as he pleased, continuously quarreling with everyone else, all talking at once, calling each other names, laughing uproariously, and raising such a racket that it made one's ears ring!

Aunt Hannah was a tall, stately woman. She was very much like one of those *grandes dames* who takes snuff from a golden snuff box decorated with a picture of a silken-hosed, white-pigtailed prince of ancient days. Obviously Aunt Hannah had once been a beautiful woman; this was apparent from her daughters, all of whom were lovely.

As soon as the Voronko youngsters entered the house, everyone ran out to meet them, creating a great din. Crowded about, they were stared at and pulled from side to side. Everyone spoke at once, bombarding their father with questions.

"Are these the hicks? Which one is this? What's that one called? Where's the little one you call 'the scamp'? Is this he? Come closer, you. Now don't be bashful! Look how shy he is! Ha, ha, ha!"

"Take a look at his cheeks. Just look at them!"

"Cheeks? No, they're peaches!"

"Let's have a good look at you, Bible boy. Come closer! Say hello nicely, Bible boy!"

Apparently Father had been unable to prevent himself from boasting that his son was a fine Bible scholar. So right there Sholom lost his old nickname and became "the Bible boy."

"Pour the Bible boy a glass of tea!"

"No, better give him an apple or pear. Let the Bible boy have a taste of Pereyaslov fruit."

"Be still, everyone! You know what just occurred to me? We'll call the Avremel brothers. They'll see how much he really knows!"

"By all means! Call the Avremel brothers. Hey, you! Run over to the Avremel brothers."

"No, you go yourself—you're bigger."

"Because I'm bigger, does that mean your legs won't carry you?"

"Because I'm smaller, do you have to order me around?"

"Listen to him!"

"Listen to *him!*"

"Shut your mouth, or I'll punch you in the nose!"

"Just try it, go ahead!"

The two adversaries, a seven-year-old with a thick nose and black eyes and a lively ten-year-old with a girlish face and blue eyes, faced one another, one swinging a shoe and the other clutching a stool, both ready for battle, like two roosters about to peck each other's eyes out. Who knows what the outcome would have been if the adults had not interfered and made peace between them by giving them both a slap. Finally a servant girl was sent to call the Avremel brothers.

The Avremel brothers finally appeared, two grown-up youths adorned with sprouting beards. They were related to Aunt Hannah on her late husband's side and lived in the house opposite hers. Their father, Itzhak Yaakov, had once been rich but had lost his fortune; he had a fine round beard and wore an earring in one of his ears. His life was spent in litigation with the government. He never looked anyone in the face, hardly ever spoke, and always smiled sourly to himself, as if to say, "How can I talk to such cattle?"

The eldest of his sons, Avremel (because of whom all of the sons were known as "the Avremel brothers") was considered the best educated of the boys, a regular know-it-all. He it was who had once examined Sholom in the little village of Voronko. But this time the Bible boy did not let his father down; he translated correctly all the passages he was given and astonished everyone by identifying the exact chapter and verse of each passage. His father stood to one side, glowing with pride. His face had lit up and the wrinkles on his forehead had disappeared. He looked like a different man standing now straight and erect.

"Give the Bible boy another apple and another pear. He deserves them," Aunt Hannah's beautiful daughters commanded. And for a long time after that the name "Bible boy" stuck to him; in the synagogue, children called him by no other name. Even adults would grab him by his ear and ask, "Tell me, now, Bible boy, where is such-and-such a verse to be found?"

And in the end it became too much of a good thing!

27 Uncle Pinney's New Home

A PIOUS HASIDIC HOME.   THE DIFFERENCE BETWEEN TWO
BROTHERS.   A TEST IN PENMANSHIP.

Uncle Pinney's home was not quite like Aunt Hannah's. The house looked different, and so did the people in it. A pious Hasidic home, it even contained an ark of the covenant. There were very many books, including the whole of the Talmud, a silver *Hanukah* candelabrum, and a long plaited wax *Havdala* candle which was lighted at the conclusion of the Sabbath.

We have already described Uncle Pinney. Though Nahum and Pinney were sons of the same father, it is difficult to find a single trait that they shared in common. Though they were both pious, both disciples of the Talna Rabbi, that is where the resemblance ended. One kept his piety to himself; the other flaunted it. One wore his ritual garments beneath his clothes; the other wore them on top. One prayed in silence, so that God alone could hear; the other raised his voice in prayer, to be heard by all.

And like father, like sons! Uncle Pinney's sons flaunted their piety, overemphasized it. They wore their coats inordinately long, the fringes of their ritual garments knee-length. His daughters wore kerchiefs chastely pulled over their faces, and never looked into the eyes of strange men. When they met a man, they blushed beet-red and began to giggle. Aunt Temmy, a pious woman with white eyebrows, was always accompanied by her mother. The two women were alike as two peas; it would have been difficult to distinguish between them had the mother's head not nodded constantly, as though she were saying, "No, no, no. . . ."

In Uncle Pinney's house, Father did not boast about his Bible boy. Here the Bible was not considered important—freethinkers alone studied the Bible. Father, however, could not help boasting about his children's penmanship. His children, he said, wrote incomparable hands.

"Now, this little fellow," pointing to his Bible boy, "has the handwriting of a scribe!"

"Very well, bring me pen and ink," Uncle Pinney commanded, rolling up his sleeves as if he were getting ready to work himself. "Quick! Pen and ink! We'll test this 'scribe's' handwriting. Hurry, hurry!"

Although Uncle Pinney's orders were observed scrupulously (like the commands of a general) and although the children, boys and girls, scurried about the room looking for pen and ink, there was neither pen nor ink to be found.

Uncle Pinney issued another order, "Well, let's have a pen!" And his sons and daughters raced out of the house, to borrow the necessary implements. Soon they returned with pen and ink. But these, alas, were not sufficient—paper was still needed.

"Paper!"

His sons and daughters again raced madly about; they fished in their pockets, searched everywhere, but not a scrap of paper was to be found.

"I have an idea! Let him write in my prayer book!" The inspired one was Itzel, Uncle Pinney's youngest son, an odd-looking boy with an egg-shaped head and long nose.

"Here. Write!" Nahum Rabinowitz ordered the Bible boy.

"What shall I write?"

"Anything you feel like writing."

The Bible boy—now scribe—dipped the pen into the ink and hesitated, confused. He didn't know what to write. He couldn't think of a thing to write! Uncle

Pinney and his family, who were eagerly surrounding him, must have thought the scribe capable of writing only when unobserved. . . . But suddenly he recalled something that Jewish children used to write in Jewish books long ago. He rolled up his sleeves, gave the pen a flourish, and once again dipped it into ink. A moment later, the following inscription appeared in the book:

Although our sages have forbidden writing in sacred books, one may do so for identification.

This was an introduction, and it was followed by the well-known Hebrew inscription:

This book belongs to someone. To whom does it belong? It belongs to him to whom it belongs. But to whom does it actually belong? To him who bought it. Who bought it? He bought it who bought it. But who actually bought it? He who paid for it. Who paid for it? He paid for it who paid for it. But who actually paid for it? He who is noble. Who is noble? He who is noble is noble. But who is really noble? Noble is the illustrious young man, called Isaac, the son of the famous and learned nobleman, Pinhas Rabinowitz, Esquire, of the city of Pereyaslov.

It is difficult to describe the furor which this inscription created, due to both style and penmanship—particularly the latter. The scribe had done his best not to let his father down. He had made the most of his talent, had worked like a beaver, and used the most beautiful, and smallest, characters he knew, characters legible only through a strong magnifying glass. In short, he had employed the art of calligraphy as he had learned it from his Voronko teacher, Reb Zorach'l. Reb Zorach'l, it should be noted, created in Voronko a school of calligraphers who, though scattered to the four corners of the globe, are to this day almost all distinguished for their beautiful penmanship.

28 Between Terms

VACATION JOYS.   ARNOLD FROM PIDVORKI.   NEW FRIENDS.
GERMISA READS THE BIBLE.   THE VORONKO HICKS SHOW
WHAT THEY CAN DO.

"Between terms"! Who can appreciate the full meaning of these words? "Leave," "recess," and "vacation" mean practically the same thing, but they do not have the significance which "between terms" has for the Jewish child.

The child who leaves the modern school on his vacation has probably spent as much time playing as studying. He has wasted time enough during the term romping with his friends; perhaps he has played *more* than he has studied. But the poor Jewish schoolboy has toiled throughout the year; from early morning till late at night he has been sitting over the Bible, studying it word by word. Then suddenly "between terms" comes! For six whole weeks he is free of *cheder,* beginning with the middle of the Jewish month of Elul, and ending with the last day of Tishri. Where can one find a better holiday? Of course there are other holidays; the Fearful Days, the Feast of the Tabernacles, the Rejoicing of the Law. . . . Now all of them would be celebrated in a new place, in the great city of Pereyaslov!

The first thing to be done "between terms" was to explore the city. As yet, the children had hardly been anywhere but to the homes of Aunt Hannah and Uncle Pinney, and the Big Synagogue, and the Old Synagogue, and the "Cold" Synagogue where Cantor Tzali prayed. There were so many other places to see! There were the rivers Altitza and Trubailo. There was the long bridge. And there was also Pidvorki, which was on the opposite side of the long bridge. Pidvorki was almost a city in its own right, but was considered a suburb of Pereyaslov. And it was here that Arnold from Pidvorki lived. Arnold from Pidvorki was a frequent visitor to Nahum Rabinowitz, and his visits often lasted several hours, which were spent talking about Maimonides, the dialogues of the Khazars, Baruch Spinoza, Moses Mendelssohn, and a host of other important people whose names Sholom soon forgot—except for one: the name "Draper," for some reason, imprinted itself on his memory forever. Dra-per. . . .

"Arnold is extremely learned," Father said. He had a very high opinion of Arnold. "If he weren't a Jew, he would have been a lawyer." Why a lawyer? And why shouldn't a Jew be a lawyer? Such things were still beyond Sholom's comprehension; he was as yet unacquainted with any expression of anti-semitism except on the part of dogs. Dogs he knew about from bitter experience. In Voronko, the peasant children had often set their dogs on him, and to this day he carries on his body souvenirs of those encounters.

The friendship between Arnold and Nahum Rabinowitz later played an important role in Sholom's life, and we shall meet him again. In the meantime, it was holiday time, and there was the opportunity to form new friendships.

On the list of sons of distinguished men was the son of Itzhak Avigdor, yellow-faced, well-groomed Moshe, who wore an alpaca suit and was very haughty. Wits said of him that he was too proud to talk to himself. Nor was he proud without reason. His father owned a handsome house with a whitewashed porch; as if this were not enough, the house was jammed with clocks and watches. When the clocks began to strike simultaneously at noon, the uproar was deafening. The father, Itzhak Avigdor, had frightening eyes and was always quarreling with someone. The children were terrified of him.

Next on the list was Ziama Koretzki, a round-shouldered boy. He was not intimate with everyone, nor did everyone seek his friendship, because his father was "shaven"; that is, he trimmed his beard. A St. Petersburg lawyer, the father wore on his nose peculiar eye glasses called pince-nez. Ziama taught his friends how to swim and ice-skate and many other things which few Jewish children knew.

Then there was the son of Israel Beneditzki, a pale sickly boy. And there was fat-cheeked Haitel Ruderman, the son of a teacher, and Avremel Zolotushkin, who was as black as a Negro; there were the sons of the Merpetzes, and the Lipsky dandies, who wore polished shoes. (It was an honor to talk to the Lipskys, for who else wore such elegant shoes on weekdays?) And there were the Kanavers, who played with dogs and teased cats. Sholom was not a friend of theirs. He was more attracted to boys like Mottel Sribny, who had long earlocks and played the violin, or volatile Elie Dodi's, who was forever laughing. He prayed in the synagogue with them, read out of the same prayer book, and made mischief with them. They mimicked Raphael the Beadle, squinting like he did when he sang out, "Eighteen guldens for the Cohan chapter! . . ." They imitated Vova Koretzki whistling through his nose, Benny Kanaver chewing tobacco, the way the shoulders of Itzhak Avigdor twitched, Sholom Vilensky's manner of snorting and patting his little beard. . . . Heavens be thanked, there were sufficient people to ridicule!

Why, there was more than enough material for mockery just in the way the teacher, Germisa, read the Torah. Sholom Rabinowitz studied him for two consecutive Sabbaths, watched him sway on one leg, screw up his pockmarked face, bare his yellow teeth, crane his long neck, flourish his pointed nose, and emit in his strange throaty voice, "See, I have set before thee this day life and good, and death and evil. . . ." It was enough to make one burst out laughing. All who saw Sholom imitate the teacher swore he was Germisa to a "T." But when Germisa learned what was going on, he was not particularly pleased. He went straight to Nahum Rabinowitz and told him all about it—that is, that he, Germisa, had heard that one of Reb Nahum's sons was parodying his reading of the Torah. This made quite an impression, and Nahum promised that as soon as the children came home he would investigate the matter. When the children arrived, Father, who had guessed that Sholom was the culprit, said, "Come here, Sholom, show me your imitation of your teacher reading the Torah."

"You mean like this!" Without a moment's hesitation, Sholom began swaying on one leg. He screwed up his face, bared his teeth, craned his neck, pushed his nose up and down, and commenced to sing in a queer throaty voice, "See, I have set before thee this day life and good. . . ."

Sholom had never seen his father laugh so hard before. He couldn't seem to stop. But when at last he finished, he coughed, wiped his eyes, and turned to the children.

"Now you see what a vacation does to you? You are loafing. Your heads get stuffed with all sorts of nonsense. You mimic your teacher. . . ." Here Father could not restrain himself and hid his face in his handkerchief. "Heaven willing, right after the Feast of the Tabernacles I'm going to find you a decent teacher and off you go to *cheder* again. It's goodbye vacations!"

Since that was the way it was going to be, the children made the most of their remaining days of freedom. They got to know all the "worst" boys, swore oaths of lifelong friendship with them, and went wild, like recruits before entering service. The Voronko bumpkins showed the big city kids that, even though they came from a village, they knew a thing or two that Pereyaslov children did not. For example, city children did not know how to spin out rhymes on a name, like, "Leibel-Kapeibel sits on a table, lives in a stable in the land of Kababel. Jake-Kapake is a fake, always eats cake in the land of Kabake. Moses-Kaposes snores when he dozes, sitting on roses in the land of Kaboses. . . ." Nor did the city children know the "Tashrak" language, which is spoken backwards. "Tnaw a pals?" meant "Want a slap?" or "Og ot eht lived!" meant "Go to the devil!" . . . Sholom could speak this language for hours, and fluently. It was marvelous to speak about someone right under his nose, and without his having the slightest idea that you were talking about him. . . .

There was no denying that Pereyaslov was a large and beautiful city. But Voronko was more fun during vacations. Such was the opinion of the Voronko children, and yet they wished their vacation in Pereyaslov would last forever.

29 *Teachers*

REB AARON HODOROVER.   A GALLERY OF TEACHERS. TEACHER MONISH AND HIS "BONE."   THE PUPILS GAMBLE IN SCHOOL.

Vacation time was not yet over and the holidays were still to come when Nahum Rabinowitz began his search for a teacher. There was quite a number to choose from. First of all, there was Germisa, whom we have mentioned, who read the Torah so well. Secondly, there was Reb Aaron Hodorover, who was very good, but who had a tendency toward tall stories. His specialty was weird tales of ancient times. A typical one was about his grandfather, an extremely strong man who was afraid of no one. One winter night, this grandfather was riding through a wood when suddenly twelve hungry wolves ran out and began chasing his sleigh. Without a moment's hesitation, Grandfather grabbed the wolves by the tail, stuck his hand into their throats, and turned them inside out! . . .

Another story told how this grandfather had once saved a whole city. One Sunday at the fair, some peasants, having drunk too much, started beating up the Jews. Grandfather, who had been right in the middle of a prayer, immediately threw off his prayer shawl and phylacteries, took the biggest peasant of all, a man called Ivan Poperilo, and, grasping him by the legs, swung him about, smacking the rest of the peasants with him. They fell to the right and to the left, like flies. When Grandfather had knocked over the last man, he released Ivan, saying, "Now you can go home, and I can return to my prayers!"

This remarkable grandfather of his was also extraordinarily absent-minded. Whenever he became immersed in thought, heaven alone could assist him. . . . One time, deep in thought, he commenced walking about his room and walked and walked . . . and then, suddenly, there he was standing on the table!

There was also a host of other teachers—Reb Yehoshua and Meyer Hersh and Yakir Simcha, the Koidenover teacher, and Fat Mendel. Unfortunately, each and every one of them had some weakness; those who knew the Talmud were weak on the Bible; and if they were strong on the Bible, they did not know the Talmud. Fat Mendel might have been the best, but he had a predilection for whipping children black and blue. When his name was mentioned, children trembled. Monish, it is true, also whipped his pupils, but he did it within reason. Fat Mendel was capable of whipping a child to death. But how he could teach! . . . Nahum promised his children that he would choose between the two.

So it seemed that they had a teacher. There remained only penmanship to consider. They had already been taught to write in Yiddish by Reb Zorach'l—but there was still Russian to be learned. Arnold from Pidvorki advised Nahum to send the children to the Jewish Government School. It would be cheaper there and better. But when Grandma Minde heard, she swore that, as long as she was alive, her grandsons would remain *Jews* —and no argument could prevail with her. There was a heated discussion on the subject of who should teach the boys penmanship. Noah Bussel was only a coachman's son-in-law . . . Itzie the Scribe wrote a good hand, but was weak in grammar . . . Itzie's brother, Abraham, was weak in both. . . . There remained only Monish. Monish had all the requirements: he knew the Bible, he had more than a nodding acquaintance with Hebrew grammar, he knew his way around the Talmud, and he wrote Russian magnificently. Of course, he didn't know what he was writing, and the syntax wasn't quite right—but that was really irrelevant. The children were still too young to study Russian grammar; first they had to learn the rudiments of Hebrew grammar—that was much more important. Nor did it matter that Monish whipped his students. If the children kept their noses to the grindstone, there would be no need to punish them. Teachers did not whip for no reason—and the children were of this opinion too. As it turned out, Monish did not resort to the ordinary punishments used by other teachers. He had something special, a little protruding bone, part of his thumb-joint, a most powerful bone which he would poke into the ribs or the shoulder blades or the temples of his students. Such a bone! It gave one mystic visions.

It was, however, a bone Sholom sought to avoid. If it had only been a question of the Talmud or the Bible, he might have been successful. The Bible he knew, and what he didn't know about the Talmud he could fake. He could manage penmanship, too. But when it came to mischief, alas, here he excelled, and so in due course he learned from experience the full potency of Monish's thumb.

But it was not because of his thumb that Monish did not satisfy Nahum Rabinowitz. Monish's acquaintance even with Hebrew grammar, it soon became clear, was superficial. When he was asked, "Reb Monish, why not teach the children grammar?" he would reply with a laugh, "Grammar, bammar, lammar . . . what's the use of grammar?" And this was too much for Nahum. The second term the children no longer had Monish for a teacher.

Now they were in the hands of a real grammarian, a man who knew the entire grammar by heart. His weakness was somewhat different—he was a meddler. Every day there was something new to occupy him; if it was not a wedding, it was a circumcision; if not a circumcision, he was celebrating the redemption of the firstborn son, or he was involved in a confirmation, or a divorce, or some legal matter. Some people might consider this a vice—but not the children. As far as they were concerned, this teacher was an angel, and his school, a paradise. They were free to do what they pleased—they could even play cards, and now not with homemade Voronko cards but with real ones. Their games were generally those which were in vogue in the Pereyaslov prisons, and their cards were prison cards—dirty, greasy, puffed up, and swollen. Poor though the cards were in quality, this did not prevent breakfasts and lunches from being gambled away, and, when a few pennies were available, they too went on cards.

The older pupils always won—boys like Ziama Koretzki. It was Ziama who initiated his young friends into all sorts of forbidden pleasures. His philosophy was summed up in three maxims:

1. Always disobey your parents.
2. Be sure to hate your teacher.
3. Never fear the Lord.

Whenever the older boys won, they made fun of the losers. This was scarcely according to the gambler's code, but then the older boys had their problems. The teacher's wife had to be bribed so as not to inform on them to her husband. Nor was she the only one; there was her son Feivel, known as "The Lip." Feivel had got his name because of his thick lips, and those lips had to be placated, flattered, sometimes fed lunches or candy —but mostly they wanted nuts. How they loved to crack the shells. It was disgusting to watch, particularly when the nuts had been bought with your own money. But what could be done? Either The Lip was fed or he told teacher. . . .

From all these teachers and all this education, Nahum Rabinowitz got little joy. On Sabbath eve he would examine his children. Always it would end up with him sighing and shaking his head. He was most concerned about his Bible boy. Evidently he expected more of him than of the rest. "Where will it end?" he would ask, "What will be the outcome? Very, very soon, before you even realize it, you'll be *bar mitzvah*—and you'll stumble over every word!"

And so he began to look for a real Talmud teacher, and at last he found one.

30 *The Talmud Teacher*

He came from Lithuania, and his name was Moshe David Ruderman. A round-shouldered man with thick
black eyebrows, he coughed continuously. He was a
great Talmudist, a master of the Bible, a genius at Hebrew grammar. As if this were not enough, he was
pious and God-fearing. Here, at last, was perfection, but
no, there was one blot on even his escutcheon! His son
attended the County School. In those days, there were
only two Jewish boys in the entire city who studied at
the County School. They were Shimon, the son of
Moshe David Ruderman, a boy who had begun growing a little black beard very early, and Chaim, the son of
the lawyer Tamarkin, a short, chubby boy with small
eyes and a hooked nose; Chaim wore his blouse over
his trousers like a peasant boy; he played ball with
Russian boys, attended synagogue only on *Yom Kippur*,
and smoked huge cigarettes in secret.

In Pereyaslov, these were the pioneers, the first swal-
lows, so to speak, of the enlightenment—the only two
Jewish children in a Russian school. At first, the Gentiles
regarded the two little Jewish boys as creatures from
another world. Then, when they were accustomed to

them, they stretched them out in the middle of the schoolyard and became fast friends with them after first smearing their lips with lard. In those days, Gentile children were innocent of Jew-baiting. The poison of anti-semitism had not yet touched them. After a young Jew had his lips smeared with lard, after he had been well beaten, he became a comrade, an equal among equals, even though his name was Abie. . . .

The business of turning Nahum's children over to Moshe David Ruderman did not proceed smoothly. When Uncle Pinney learned that Nahum's children were to be taught by a teacher whose son attended the County School, he was horrified.

"A fine teacher you've found for your children!" he shouted, "It's not enough that this Lithuanian teaches grammar and stylistic niceties—but he's actually handed his own son over to the Gentiles, for conversion!"

Nahum laughed and gently explained that grammar and style had nothing to do with heresy, and that it was a long step from the County School to the monastery.

"All right, we'll see who's right!"

It was evidently destined that Uncle Pinney should prove himself a prophet.

One Sabbath, the rumor spread through the city that the two Jewish boys who attended the County School were to be baptized. Of course, at first no one would believe it. "What will they say next? People are capable of inventing anything!" But where there is smoke, there is fire. Later that Sabbath, the panic spread, and the whole Jewish population of the city rushed to the monastery. "You want to see a sight? Go to the monastery, and you'll see these two fine fellows from the County School standing on the roof, with their heads uncovered, stuffing bread and lard into themselves!"

No one thought of asking, of course, how from a distance you could see that it was lard, and not butter or honey, which was on the bread. But the whole city had gone stark raving mad, although they weren't quite so indignant about Chaim. "Tamarkin's son's understandable. From the day he was conceived he was a *Goy*. His father's no good. He doesn't eat *kosher* food and he doesn't observe any of the laws. . . . But Moshe David's son! A God-fearing man and a Hebrew teacher —the best Hebrew teacher in town! How could such a thing have happened?"

But it turned out that there were plenty of people who had always known it would happen. Why, it was as clear as day! If you send a child to the County School, it is just as good as saying you want him to be a Gentile. If you send him there, you can't require that he wear the ritual *arba kanfoth,* and, if he skips a prayer or two, you have to wink at it. No thrashing him to see it doesn't happen again. . . . Such was the opinion of these people.

The Jewish community assembled to consult further. How to save the two Jewish boys? They rushed here and there, trying to find someone with influence, besieging the authorities. . . . Naturally, Uncle Pinney worked harder than anyone. He rolled up his sleeves, unloosened his venerable beard, and bustled about, sweating profusely. Nor did he eat or drink until the two boys were removed from the monastery.

The end of the story occurred several years later, when Chaim Tamarkin actually became a convert. Shimon Ruderman, however, was sent to Zhitomer, placed in a rabbinical seminary at public expense, and not only graduated from it, but actually became a rabbi in Lubni, a town not far from Pereyaslov.

"Well, who was right? Can we hope that you'll take your children away from that teacher now?" Uncle Pinney asked his brother. Uncle Pinney was very pleased with the way things had turned out. He had succeeded in saving two Jewish children from conversion; his nephew would no longer study with a teacher who knew grammar and had a son in the County School; and, what's more, his suspicions had been justified: if a Jewish child studied in a Russian school, he would sooner or later be converted.

But Uncle Pinney hoped for too much. His brother obstinately held his ground; he would not think of taking his children away from such an excellent teacher.

"What have I got against him? He's had his share of sorrow. Must he, in the bargain, be deprived of his livelihood?"

As he listened to his brother, a bitter smile came to the lips of Uncle Pinney. It seemed to say, "I hope I'm no prophet here, but the things that will happen to your children. . . ." He rose silently, kissed the *mezuzah,* and left, slamming the door behind him.

31 Cheder in Those Days

A PICTURE OF THE SCHOOLROOM.   THE PUPILS HELP THEIR
TEACHER AND HIS WIFE.   TEACHER READS SERMONS.   HIS
SERMONS LEAD TO NEW TRANSGRESSIONS.

No, the children were not taken away from that excellent, though unfortunate, teacher. They remained with Ruderman for a second term and for a third. Everyone was content: the teacher with his students, the students with their teacher, and Father with both students and teacher.

The children were happiest of all. At last the good Lord had sent them a teacher who did not whip them. This teacher did not even know what a whip was for. Once in a very rare while, when some child had tried him too sorely, Reb Ruderman would lose patience. When this happened, the guilty boy would be laid on the bench, and Reb Ruderman would take off his soft velvet skullcap and spank him lightly with it—that was all!

There was another wonderful thing about him. In his home he had a millstone with which he ground grain. This machine had a wheel with a handle, and on top of the machine lay a bag of buckwheat turned upside down. When one turned the handle, the wheel revolved and the buckwheat spilled slowly into a box; from the box it fell onto a stone; the stone milled slowly, removing the chaff.

The most important work, of course, was turning the handle. The harder one turned, the more flour you got, and there were plenty of volunteers for this job. Everyone wanted to help poor Moshe David, who could not manage on teaching alone and had to have a side line. The man mills the flour; the woman bakes the cakes. Do you think there is no work to baking? Here too the children would lend a hand—if not in the actual baking, then in the kneading. Rye honey-cake has to be kneaded for a long time, until it pulls as only honey batter can. And who can knead better than school-children? There were so many candidates for this honor of pounding the dough that they often ended up pounding each other. Everyone wanted to be first.

The reader must not be surprised that schoolchildren performed such tasks as milling grain and kneading dough. They had done much coarser work for their Voronko teachers. At Reb Zorach'l's, the sons of Nahum Vevik's had scrubbed floors beautifully; they had removed the slops, fetched water from the village well, and had even nursed the teacher's baby—not to mention taking chickens to the ritual slaughterer. A child was honored to help his teacher's wife pluck a chicken. Any chore rather than study! And here, I believe, is the proper place to describe the *cheder* of those days so that future generations may know how, and in what kind of surroundings, children were brought up.

Imagine a small peasant hut on "chicken legs," slightly lopsided, sometimes thatched, and sometimes without any roof at all—hatless, as it were. One small window, two at the most. The panes have been knocked out, and the holes are covered with paper or plugged with small pillows. The floor is earthen, smeared with clay or covered with sand—the latter on Sabbaths and holidays. The largest part of the room is occupied by an oven and an oven bench on which the teacher sleeps. His children sleep on top of the oven. Next to one wall stands his wife's bed with a mountain of large pillows at its head and smaller pillows piled almost to the ceiling. There, upon the white-sheeted bed, you sometimes find a leaf of dough, or some biscuits or buns (if the teacher's wife does any baking), and once in a while a child. Under the oven is a chicken coop where fowl are raised —to sell, naturally. Next to a crooked-bellied wall stands a cupboard where bread and pots are kept. On top of the cupboard are a pile of kitchen utensils, a sieve, a scrubbing brush, and the like. At the entrance stand pokers, shovels, a large slop pail (always full to the brim), and a wooden tub which is always leaking. A hand towel, always wet, hangs near the door.

In the middle of the room there are two long benches and a long table. This is the "school" proper, where the teacher studies with his students. Everyone shouts—children as well as teacher. So do the teacher's own children. They shout as they play on top of the oven. The teacher's wife, busy in the "kitchen," shouts at the children to stop shouting. The chickens cackle under the oven; the cat has jumped down from the oven bench and sneaked into the coop and frightened the hens. . . .

Such was the appearance of a Voronko *cheder,* and the school in the vast city of Pereyaslov was not much better. Both the Pereyaslov and the Voronko teacher studied with their students; in winter, both dressed in a cotton gown and a velvet skullcap, and, in summer, in an *arba kanfoth* and a wide-sleeved shirt. In winter, after his midday nap, the Pereyaslov teacher drank limewater rather than tea, and, in summer, cold water out of a wooden cup, previously strained through one of his shirtsleeves. He blessed the water very solemnly and all his students would echo, "Amen." Should one of the students bring him fruit, the Pereyaslov teacher would recite the blessing to "the Creator of the fruit of the tree," and there would be the inevitable "Amen" from the students.

As for the students, they were happy to do anything but study. Studying had become an unbearable bore. They studied all day long, and in the winter during the evenings as well. School work started as soon as they woke at dawn. They even studied on Sabbath afternoons, and, when they were not studying, they listened to the teacher's sermons.

These seemed to have come straight out of Dante, for their subject matter was exclusively the tortures of Hell. One experienced the horrifying "shaking of the tombs." One heard the Angel of Hell softly steal up to a sinner and watched him rip open the unfortunate's belly, pull out his insides, and toss them into his face, "Sinner, thy name?" Two torturing angels might take a child, so these sermonizers said, and throw him like a ball from one end of the world to the other. If one had ever told a lie, he would be hanged by his tongue with a nail, like the carcass of an animal. If the rite of washing one's fingernails had been omitted, two angels would tear out one's nails with pincers. If one had ever pared his nails on a Friday and dropped a paring carelessly on the floor, one would be sent back to earth to look for it.

Those punishments were for petty transgressions. What of really important sins? Rushing through the morning prayer, for instance? Or skipping the evening prayer altogether, forgetting to say one's prayers at night? Having an evil thought or daydream? Here no mercy would be shown one! Penance, prayers, the giving of alms—these helped in this world, but not in the next. As far as the next world was concerned, it was already too late.

"There you'll be like all the other sinners. Off you'll go into the eternal flames, into a boiling cauldron, into Gehenna. Do you hear me, you rascals, into Gehenna!" Thus would our teacher's Sabbath sermon end. The children listened, wept, and were penitent. But as soon as they had left *cheder,* the other world, with its Gehenna and its torturing angels, disappeared like a passing shadow. One by one the old sins returned, the morning prayer was shortened, the evening and bedtime prayers omitted. . . . What was handwashing to them, or prayers, when outside the sun was shining and shadows were climbing the walls? The shadows nodded to them, called to them, "Come out, children, come out! There's joy out here, and freedom! One leap, and you are at the bridge. Another, and you are on the other side. The brook murmurs so sweetly over here, and the grass is

so green and the flowers so yellow, such fine birds are flying and such nice grasshoppers jumping. . . ."

Yes, over there green fields invited one to throw one-self down on the soft fragrant earth. . . . But then Father or Mother, an older sister or a brother would come. "Have you said your prayers? Back to school, you truant, back to school!"

32   The Bar Mitzvah

THE RIDDLE.   GRANDMA MINDE SUPERVISES.   THE BAR MITZVAH IS A GREAT SUCCESS. A GALLERY OF PEREYASLOV TYPES.   MOTHER'S TEARS.

When one considers the odd sort of teachers the children had and the peculiar sort of school they attended, even having to assist the teacher's wife, and when one adds to this the demands their family made upon them, the endless chores and errands they had to perform for their parents and sisters and brothers, it is difficult to understand how the children managed to learn as much as they did. Nor must we forget that time had to be found for all sorts of games and amusements; during the summer there was swimming and, in the winter, playing cards and buttons and just wandering about the city. We must remember also the fact that they were continually hoodwinking their teacher and their father, and even the rabbi who came to examine them twice a year. Where did Sholom acquire the ingenuity to fool the entire Jewish community of the city, gathered to celebrate his *bar mitzvah?* He clearly recalls that he did not understand one word of the intricate and complex sermon he prepared weeks in advance of this great day. Yet the whole city sang with praises after he had delivered it. Other fathers were envious, and mothers sighed to have such a child.

It was a holiday, a marvelous holiday in Nahum Rabinowitz's home. Endless hands were busy preparing, all under the command of Grandma Minde, who, in her Sabbath frock and headband, really looked like the head of a regiment. It was she who had decided whom to invite and whom to pass over; who was to sit in the places of honor and who in more humble places; what dishes were to be served as well as what kind of brandy and wines. She quarreled with everyone, scolded everyone, did not even spare the hero of the occasion. He, she insisted, should act like a *man;* he should not bite his nails—certainly not in the presence of the guests— nor should he laugh or make the other children giggle. In short, he should not behave like a rascal.

"The Lord has seen fit to bring you to the day of your *bar mitzvah;* it's high time you became a human being!" So Grandma admonished him, wetting her fingers and smoothing those remnants of his earlocks which she had been able to rescue from her son. Nahum Rabinowitz had decided long since to cut them off entirely, but Grandma Minde would not hear of it. "After I die and my eyes can no longer see it," she said, "you can make *Goyim* of your children. But as long as I'm alive, I want to see some sign of Jewishness upon their heads!"

The entire family attended the celebration, along with the great crowd that was invited to come to the *bar mitvah* straight from the synagogue. Of course, Moshe David Ruderman was there, dressed in his Sabbath clothes and with a faded velvet cap which sat on his head like a pancake. He conducted himself very modestly, sitting apart from everyone. Ruderman had greatly fallen in his own estimation since the scandal involving his son. He scarcely touched the wine and the refreshments, and sat huddled up, softly coughing into the broad sleeves of his Sabbath coat.

But when the long-awaited moment arrived and the hero of the occasion stood on a table and began his sermon, suddenly Ruderman came to life. His shoulders straightened and he raised his thick black eyebrows and looked at Sholom; and then his thumb began moving up and down like a conductor's baton.

As for Sholom, he was terrified. His mouth felt dry, and little sparks danced before his eyes. It seemed as if he were walking on ice and that any minute the ice would crack—one false step and he would crash through, bringing the audience with him. But then he felt his teacher's eye upon him and was hypnotized by his stare. He saw his teacher's thumb moving up and down, and he gathered courage. He moved forth boldly.

Now he was walking on a steel bridge, and warmth permeated his limbs. The sermon rolled off his lips without an error.

Even in the middle of the sermon, as he moved his thumb in time to his teacher's, Sholom managed to observe the guests. He noticed every expression, every turn of the head.

There was Itzhak Avigdor, his shoulders twitching as usual, and old Yehoshua Scribny, supposedly not a day under one hundred, whose tongue rolled about in his mouth like the tongue of a bell, for he hadn't a single tooth left. There was Yehoshua's son Berkeh, no youngster himself; his eyes were shut, and his head tipped to one side. Close to Berkeh, Sholom saw Osher Naidiss, whom everyone called "Mushy Osher" because he was so broad and fat; his silk coat was splitting at the seams, and he was gray as a pigeon. And near Osher was Yossi Fruchstein, with his large false teeth, glittering eyeglasses, and thin little beard. He played chess with Nahum Rabinowitz and read worldly books like *The Mysteries of Paris* and the ancient geography textbook called *The Paths of the World,* and was considered a freethinker. Next to Yossi stood his younger brother, Michael Fruchstein, a clever, smooth young man. He was a dissenter—that is, he permitted his Christian servant girl to put out the candles on Sabbath and only respected men like Moshe Berger and Benny Kanaver, who, as everyone knew, looked the other way when they were young and let the barber trim their beards. Israel Benditzky was also among the guests. He had once been known as Israel the Fiddler, but now he owned a house of his own and a prominent seat in the synagogue. He wore a broad, black, shiny beard, and, although he would now and then play at some important wedding, no one dared call him "Fiddler" now, even behind his back. He had become an important man, a man of dignity. When he laughed, he showed all his small, beautifully formed, white teeth. As he spoke, Sholom even spotted Raphael the Beadle. Standing slightly bent, and squinting as always, he was completely immersed in the sermon and looked as if any moment he would bang on the table and sing out, "Ten guldens! . . ."

All the faces were solemn, but most solemn of all was Uncle Pinney's. He sat in the place of honor next to Sholom's father, clad in a silk Sabbath coat, girdled with a broad silk belt, a blue satin cap on his head. His head cocked to one side, Uncle Pinney stared at Sholom as if to say, "All right, he knows his sermon, but does he say his prayers regularly? Does he wash his hands before eating? Does he keep the Sabbath? . . . Those are things we can be a little skeptical about! . . ."

Sholom's father, however, glowed with pleasure. One could see that this was the happiest man in the world. He held his head high; his lips moved, repeating every word his son uttered. And as he repeated his son's sermon under his breath, he glanced about at the other guests.

And Mother, little Haya Esther, wearing her silk Sabbath kerchief, stood modestly to one side, quite unnoticed among the rest of the women. Enraptured and sighing softly, she pulled nervously at her fingers. Gem-like tears rolled down her happy face, a white, young face that had faded too soon. . . .

What did those tears mean? Were they tears of pride and joy? Or was she weeping because times were bad? Or did her mother's heart perhaps prophesy that the young hero of this *bar mitzvah,* whose voice was now ringing out so beautifully, would soon say *Kaddish* for her soul?

Who knows why a mother weeps?

Part II

Part II

33 *The Youth*

THE HERO BECOMES A MAN AMONG MEN.   BROTHER HERSHEL
GETS ENGAGED TO BE MARRIED.   AN EXAMINATION WITH A
PROMPTER'S HELP.   A PHYLACTERY BAG, A WATCH, AND A
BRIDE.

"Now with God's grace you've become a young man,
and it's high time that you acted like one. Before you
know it, you'll be engaged to be married. . . ."

This was part of the lecture delivered to Sholom on
the day following that solemn Sabbath, as the teacher
helped him bind the phylacteries on his arm. The arm-
box was bound on his left arm so tightly that the boy's
fingers became blue and swollen. The large head-box,
apparently eager to slip down, kept gliding to a spot
almost midway between his eyes but slightly off to one
side. Sholom found it difficult to keep his balance; he
could not move with ease, nor did he dare look at his
friends, who crowded about him eagerly to watch him
pray in phylacteries for the first time. To be quite
frank, if it had not been for his friends, this was the one
occasion on which Sholom would have prayed with all

his heart and soul. He enjoyed this ceremony; he liked the word *Ve-eirastich* [and it will betroth thee] in the prayer; he liked the pleasant smell of the new leather bands; he liked being called a "young man"; and he was proud of the fact that he could now be part of a *minyan* [the group of ten adult men necessary for a religious service]. He was a full-fledged Jew now, the equal of every adult, a man among men. Even Raphael the Beadle squinted at him with different expression; he almost seemed to respect him. As for his friends, they envied him as he had once envied his older brother, Hershel, when he had been confirmed. But the truth was that he envied Hershel less for the ceremony than for the events which had followed close upon it. Soon after the *bar mitzvah*, Hershel had become engaged; his fiancée had given him an embroidered phylactery bag, and her father had presented him with a silver watch. Both the betrothal and the fate of the watch deserve to be recorded.

Hershel was an exceptional boy, handsome and extraordinarily neat, but he had no head for studies. Since, however, he came from an excellent family and was the son of Nahum Rabinowitz, he was offered a number of excellent matches.

One day, a handsome black-bearded man arrived from the town of Vasilkov. He was one of the fathers who wanted to make a match and was accompanied by a young man with a diminutive red beard, an examiner. The examiner was reputed to be a connoisseur of Hebrew and the Bible. This fellow had a very aggressive character, was something of a quibbler, and delighted in worrying a body to death. And immediately he started to show off his immense learning. He began by cornering Hershel's teacher and starting a lengthy debate on the subject of grammar. Every statement the poor teacher made was immediately refuted. Then he took the offensive and asked the teacher to explain why, in Ecclesiastes, "Dead flies *causes* the ointment of the apothecary to send forth a stinking savor" is written in the singular and not in the plural. The teacher did not reply, but retaliated by asking why, also in Ecclesiastes, "Remember thy *Creators*" is written in the plural and not in the singular. But now the examiner came at him from a different direction. "Tell me precisely where you can find 'And when they went from nation to nation.'" By this time, the teacher was utterly confused and replied, "Why, that's from the prayer, 'Give thanks to the Lord, call upon His name.'" This did not satisfy the young man. "In which book of the Bible?" Still more confused, the teacher replied, "Oh, it must be somewhere in Psalms." There was a burst of laughter from the redhead. "I beg your pardon, sir, it isn't 'somewhere in Psalms.' It is true we do find it in one of the Psalms, but you can also find it in Chronicles!"

Drops of sweat stood out on the teacher's brow. He was completely overwhelmed. "That's a clever one for you!" he said to the children, wiping the moisture from his forehead with the hem of his coat. "If he examines Hershel that way, we can forget about the engagement!"

But since the teacher had an interest in this match— or, to be more exact, not so much in the match as in the matchmaker fees—he came up with a brilliant plan.

He whispered something to Hershel's younger brother, Sholom, and hid him behind the sofa upon which Hershel was to sit. Then the matchmakers seated themselves around the three-legged table, and the redhead sprang to the attack. Mother calmly kept on with her business of putting cakes and brandy on the table; evidently she had no doubt of the outcome.

"Now tell me, my dear young man, where do we find the sentence, 'He that is ready to slip with his feet is as a lamp despised in the thought of him that is at ease?' "

"In the Book of Job," came a whisper from behind the sofa.

"In the Book of Job," Hershel answered glibly, and he spoke with assurance.

"That's correct, in the Book of Job. . . . And now tell me whether you know of another word in the Bible with the same root as *'ashtut'* [thoughts]," the examiner continued.

" 'In that very day his thoughts perish'—it's in the Psalms," squeaked the prompter, and Hershel echoed him word for word.

"Very fine indeed! Well, that finishes the Bible," the examiner said, and he cast a glance at the table at which little Haya Esther was occupying herself with cakes and jellies. "Now we'll take a look at grammar. Suppose we analyze the verb 'to perish' in Hebrew. What kind of verb is it? How is it conjugated?"

Sholom softly whispered the answers from behind the sofa, and Hershel repeated them after him. "It is an intransitive verb of simple construction, and it is conjugated as follows. . . ."

"Enough, enough!" exclaimed the examiner with a pleased expression on his face. He rubbed his hands, looked again at the table spread with food, and said to the fiancée's father, who was beaming with joy, "Congratulations! You can see for yourself that the lad is just brimming with knowledge! . . . Well, shall we have a bite? . . ."

Who knows whether the parents were aware of the ruse, or whether the secret was known only to the teacher and his two pupils? Possibly even the examiner knew what was up. In any event, both parties were satisfied, and no one felt cheated.

And now we come to the story of the watch. Naturally, right after the examination, Mother went to have a look at the bride, and she was satisfied with what she found. So the betrothal was celebrated, the necessary documents were signed, the necessary dishes were broken, and the future father-in-law presented his future son-in-law with a silver watch. As often as there are minutes in an hour, the bridegroom would take his watch out and look at it. Nothing made him so happy as to be asked the time. It was his most cherished possession. There was no place safe enough for it when he went to bed. Before going to synagogue, he would seek out the most obscure cupboards in the house in which to hide it. He was in constant terror that it would be stolen.

Then one day our excessively neat young man decided to brush his suit. In those days, the more stylish suits were made of hairy serge, and this serge had a remarkable capacity when it came to dust. The bridegroom took his flexible reed cane, hung the suit over the stoop of the house, and began beating out the dust with his cane. Suddenly he recalled where he had left his watch, and feverishly snatched up his suit. Out of it came a fine powder of silver, porcelain, and glass, along with a jumble of tiny wheels. Promises of a new watch did not console the bridegroom; he was completely prostrate with grief. . . .

After Sholom's *bar mitzvah,* he considered himself a man, just like his brother. Three things he wanted: a bag for his phylacteries, a watch, and a bride. The bride that he imagined was a beautiful princess; she was one of the lovely ladies of Shmulik's stories. So real was she for him that he often saw her in his dreams. And one day, very soon after his confirmation, he met her in person and, with all the fervor of adolescent passion, fell in love with her.

34 First Love

THE SHULAMITE OF THE SONG OF SONGS. A DANGEROUS RIVAL. SQUEAKY BOOTS AND THE FRENCH LANGUAGE. THE VIOLIN. SWEET DREAMS.

Had they not met many times afterward, the hero of this biography would believe that the girl who bewitched him in his fourteenth year was only a figment of his imagination, a dream of his childhood. Her name was Rose, and she was never by herself. She was always accompanied by a host of admirers; these were boys from the wealthiest Jewish families, along with an occasional army officer. For a Russian officer to be seen walking with a Jewish girl was enough of a sensation to set the whole city agog. Few girls would have permitted themselves such a liberty, fewer would have been forgiven it. But all things were permissible for Rose, because she was *Rose,* the only Jewish girl in the city who played the piano, spoke French, talked freely, and laughed boldly. Who could compare to Rose? And she came of an excellent family. Her father was one of the most distinguished and aristocratic men in the city. Gossip was that he had been in the habit of shaving in his youth, but now that he was old and gray, he wore a beard and eyeglasses and had pouches under his eyes. His daughter inherited the pouches, but they were very becoming when accompanied by her lovely blue eyes. Her handsome arched brows, her Greco-Jewish nose, her milk-white face, her small but beautifully majestic figure won the heart of that innocent daydreamer, Sholom Rabinowitz. After one glance from those lovely Shulamite eyes, he was hopelessly in love.

Oh, yes, she definitely was Shulamite, the Shulamite of the Song of Songs, and her beautiful blue eyes penetrated to the soul. But, alas, she glanced at Sholom only once—well, twice at the most. The first glance came merely by accident; she passed him in the street one Sabbath afternoon with a whole crowd of admirers at her heels. Among them was that most fortunate young man, Chaim Fruchstein. Chaim, Yossi Fruchstein's only son, had very short legs, compensated for by a nose which was long enough and covered by pimples in the bargain, and as red as a raspberry. His teeth were also monstrously large. Yet he dressed like a fop. He wore squeaky patent leather shoes with very high heels to make him appear taller, and a vest as white as new-fallen snow. He combed his hair with a part in the middle, and incidentally always doused it with such strong perfume that you could smell it a mile away. He was Rose's favorite, and, because he was Yossi Fruchstein's son, the city took it for granted that they were engaged. Yossi Fruchstein was a rich man, and, naturally, wealth should mate with wealth. What was more, he was the only youth in Pereyaslov who spoke French. Could any match be more appropriate—both spoke French! And she played the piano and he played the violin, and when they played together, one could stand and listen all night long. . . .

Many a summer's night, Sholom did stand outside of Rose's house, listening to the heavenly sounds that issued from the open windows. Oh, what emotions he felt then! It was bliss mingled with pain—pain because it was not he who was playing the violin while Rose played the piano. He blessed the hands that drew such sounds from a dead instrument, and he cursed the day he had been born the son of Nahum Rabinowitz; he should have been born a Fruchstein. For was not Chaim a rich man's son, and he, Sholom, so wretchedly poor, too poor to ask his parents to buy him squeaky, patent leather shoes with high heels? The shoes he had were worn out; the heels were crooked, the soles were full of holes. And suppose he were to hint that he wanted patent leather shoes. There would be the inevitable question, "What for?" If he were to add that they must be *squeaky* shoes, he'd certainly catch it!

But if he had the treasure, Shmulik the Orphan's treasure! But there was no treasure. Or, rather, the treasure existed, but it was so hard to find; it was buried so deep! The harder one looked for it, the deeper it buried itself. . . . And once again Sholom cursed the day he was born a Rabinowitz and not a Fruchstein. He grew to hate Chaim, short-legged Chaim and his long nose, Chaim whom the Lord had endowed with all blessings —squeaky boots, French, and a violin.

And one night, as Sholom stood beneath Rose's window, he swore an oath by the moon and the stars. He swore that, come what may, he would learn to play the violin. He swore that with his playing he would put all the Chaims in the world to shame. And he would learn to speak French as well as Chaim and become as good as Chaim in everything. With God's grace he would be better. . . . Then he would walk straight into Rose's house and say to her in the words of the Song of Songs, " 'Return, return, O Shulamite! . . .' Turn to me, O Rose; for a moment turn thy face to me and listen to me play the violin!" He would draw his bow across the slender strings, and she would listen, overwhelmed. "Who taught you?" she would ask. And he would reply, "I just taught myself." And Chaim Fruchstein would stand at a distance, green with envy. He would approach Rose and say something in French to her, but Sholom would interrupt, saying (also in French, of course), "Be careful what you say, Reb Chaim, because I understand every word!" Chaim would gape, and Rose the Shulamite would ask, "So you speak French, too? Who taught you?" And Sholom would reply as before, "I just taught myself." Then Rose the Shulamite would rise and, taking Sholom by the hand, bid him to go with her. And together they would promenade on the sidewalks of Pereyaslov. They would converse in French and at their heels would be Rose's admirers, with Chaim Fruchstein in their midst. The whole city would point at them, and ask, "Who is that happy couple?" "What, you don't know? That's Rose and her sweetheart!" "Who is her sweetheart?" "Why, that's the Voronko Bible boy, Sholom Nahum Vevik's, Sholom Rabinowitz!" Sholom would hear every word, but would pretend he did not. He would walk on and on, hand in hand with beautiful Rose, and look into her blue eyes, which would return his gaze laughingly. He would feel her warm little hand in his own and hear the beating of his heart: tick-tock, tick-tock! But no, there would be another sound—his boots would have started to squeak! Now that would be something to astonish everyone. He would have taught himself to play the violin and to speak French. He would have worked day and night to master these accomplishments. But who would have taught his boots to squeak? They, themselves? He pressed down hard with both feet, and received a punch in the back. "Why are you kicking like a horse?" his older brother asked.

He awoke, in bed with his brother. Had it been only a dream? . . .

But the dream pursued him. All day long he thought of it, building fancy upon fancy. The dream merged with reality, reality with the dream. He can not remember how long that continued, but then a guest arrived in Pereyaslov, a dreadful guest whose name was plague. He flew like a hurricane over the city, laying waste homes. Nor did he spare the home of Nahum Rabinowitz. Because of him, Sholom forgot his lovely Shulamite. His passion for her melted away like a dream, like a shadow, like a mist. . . .

The guest was cholera.

35 Cholera

THE PLAGUE. THE "RUBBERS." MOTHER HAS A BAD DREAM. GRANDMA MINDE TAKES CHARGE AND HELPS THE DOCTORS. MOTHER'S DEATH. UNCLE PINNEY FORBIDS WEEPING ON THE SABBATH.

As if through spite, it began during the summer, just after Passover. It was not very severe at first, but after Pentecost, when the fruit had ripened and gooseberries had become cheap, it really raged. More and more frequently you heard words like "plague," "epidemic," "cholera." The word "cholera" was always accompanied by a curse. Terror swept the city.

Of course, only the adults were deeply concerned. For the youngsters it was something of a holiday. The elders were forever preparing special food and drink for the children; they felt their foreheads and examined their tongues. At length the schools were closed until, with God's grace, the epidemic should cease. But it was in no hurry to go.

Whatever the citizens possibly could do, they did. There was, first of all, "rubbing." A society of "rubbers" was quickly formed. Their task was to put the stricken to bed and rub them all over with brushes, and this saved many. The chief citizens volunteered as "rubbers," and the city was divided into districts. Sholom regarded the "rubbers" with great awe; in his eyes they were heroes. It was obvious that they feared neither the cholera nor death, and they encouraged one another with smiles, inspired themselves with brandy, and prayed to the Lord to be merciful and halt the epidemic.

The Rabinowitz family was, naturally, among the "rubbers." When Nahum Rabinowitz returned from his district in the evening, he always brought news: whom he had rubbed that day; how many times he had rubbed them; who had responded to the treatment and who had not. . . . Everyone stood around him listening respectfully, curious and yet fearful. Little Haya Esther cracked her finger-joints and glanced anxiously at her host of children. Once she said casually, "Heaven forbid that the cholera should enter this house!" Nahum smiled and replied that cholera was not the sort of illness which one brought into the house. "Cholera visits only those chosen by fate."

And apparently little Haya Esther had been chosen. One morning she awoke and told Grandma Minde that she had had a strange dream. She had dreamed it was Friday evening, and she was blessing the candles. Suddenly, Fruma Sarah, who had died of the epidemic only a week before, appeared to her. Fruma Sarah suddenly blew the candles out. . . . Grandma Minde listened, laughed, and naturally interpreted the dream as a good omen. But one could see by their pale faces that both women were terrified.

Later, Mother took to her bed, asked for a mirror, looked into it, and said to Grandma, "Mother, it looks serious—see my fingernails?" Of course, Grandma ridiculed the idea, and wished all these evil dreams to descend upon the heads of her enemies, but nevertheless, in secret, she sent the older children to look for Father, who was out rubbing in his district. She did not, however, wait for him to come. She put large kettles of water into the oven and did everything humanly possible for the sick woman, nor did she fail to send for Doctor Kazachkovsky, the best doctor in town, a stout, red-faced Russian who was so healthy, people said he would die on his feet. But even though Kazachkovsky was the best physician in town, Grandma Minde also called Yankel, the assistant surgeon, because he was a Jew and she could make herself better understood with him. Although Yankel was a mere assistant, he wore a real doctor's cape and he wrote prescriptions, read Latin, and also, like a real doctor, took money. When you slipped a coin into his hand, he would pretend he didn't want it, but when it was safe in his pocket, he fingered it carefully to discover its value. If the fee was too small, he would ask for more, but very subtly, with a smile, meanwhile patting his long hair and adjusting the eyeglasses on his nose. . . .

Grandma Minde retired with him to her room, first taking care to send the children out of doors. She remained closeted with him until Father arrived, more dead than alive, and then she fell upon Father and scolded him unmercifully. There was something comical about the way he sought to defend himself against her. But those who have not seen Grandma Minde as she was in those days cannot understand. The woman was a general—no, a field marshal. A dark green silk kerchief, decorated with silver apples, was tied about her head, and the sleeves of her woolen dress had been rolled up to her elbows. She wore a black alpaca apron over her gown, and this, along with her well-scrubbed hands and her stern old wrinkled face, created the illusion that she was officiating at a wedding, and not in a sickroom where her daughter-in-law lay ill with cholera.

In fact, it seemed as if it were not Mother but Grandma Minde who was battling the Terrible Angel whose great black wings rustled overhead. Yes, one could hear him in the room, but he was not yet visible. The children did not quite understand what was happening, but they instinctively felt that it was something momentous. On Grandma's face they read: "Death wants to take Mother away from her children, but I shall not allow it! The Lord will help me." When she said it, you believed it—you had to believe Grandma Minde!

Doctor Kazachkovsky came to visit Mother when she was already hopelessly ill, a fact confirmed by his flushed face, which had turned even redder than usual. Grandma Minde put all the children in a row, with the eldest—a bearded young man already married—first; and the smallest—a baby girl scarcely a year old—last. When the doctor came out of the sickroom, she fell at his feet, kissed his hands, and drew him toward the line of children. "Doctor, look how many little worms she will leave behind if she should die, God forbid! Doctor, take pity on these little worms!" Her words would have melted a stone, and they did the doctor. "What can I do?" he asked. Was he not doing everything possible? "Here's whom you should ask for help," and he pointed toward the ceiling. But Grandma Minde didn't need that advice. She had already been to the synagogue. She had hired people to read the Psalms day and night. And she had visited the cemetery, trusting in the powers of her ancestors to intervene for her. . . . A mother like her Nahum's wife must not make a widower of her son, orphans of her grandchildren. "A saint like Haya Esther *must* not die! No, dear Lord, you are merciful, you will not allow it! . . ."

Yet, though God was merciful and kind, little Haya Esther never rose from her sickbed. She died on a Sabbath morning, while Jews were still praying in the synagogue.

She died. . . . This was a second blow for the children; the first had been the death of their teacher, Moshe the Slaughterer. Their suffering was great. True, their mother had not been as gentle as most mothers. She had slapped them plenty, for "Children shouldn't be greedy! . . . Children shouldn't get into people's way! . . . Children shouldn't show their teeth and neigh like horses! . . ." (meaning that children shouldn't laugh). But the children had laughed all the same—for how could one keep from laughing if something was funny? Laughter had cost them dear; they had paid for it with red ears and swollen cheeks, for Mother's small, strong hands could make themselves felt. . . .

But now all that was forgotten. All they remembered was how Mother would dig into her pocket to find a penny for each of them; how Mother would feed them sulphur and molasses the first day of each month; how her little hand would feel their foreheads, their pulses, and pat their cheeks when they were ill; how every Friday she would wash their hair; how on Passover Eve she would laugh when the children became tipsy with wine. . . . This they remembered, and each child buried his face in his pillow, crying bitterly. When they heard Father weep, their sobs became louder and stronger. How was it possible for *Father* to weep! . . . Grandma Minde was also weeping, and conversing with the Lord to the melody of a prayer. Why did he not take her, Grandma Minde, rather than this young twig, the mother of so many little worms? . . . The comparison of children to worms provoked an involuntary smile from them—why *worms?* . . .

Suddenly, the door opened and Uncle Pinney and

his sons burst into the house, come straight from the Old Synagogue and crying out loudly, "Good Sabbath!" When Uncle Pinney saw everyone weeping and wailing, he began to scold Father and Grandma Minde. "What's this! Weeping on the Sabbath? Have you gone mad? Have you forgotten that it's forbidden to weep on the Sabbath? Nahum, what's the matter with you? You mustn't, it's the holy Sabbath! Whatever happens, you must remember the Sabbath!" As he said this, he turned away, pretending to be wiping his nose, and stealthily cast a glance into the room where Mother was lying covered with black. He dried his eyes quickly, so that no one should see he was crying, but now he spoke more gently, and tears trembled in his voice.

"Stop it, Nahum. Come, come, stop it! It's against the Law. It's Sab. . . ."

Uncle Pinney did not finish the word. The tears that he had swallowed stuck in his throat. Unable to control himself, he sat down at the table, laid his head on his left arm, and burst into tears, wailing in a shrill voice, like a little child:

"Haya Esther, Haya Esther. . . ."

36 The Week of Mourning

Never did the author of this biography long so for the
treasure as when he and his father and his sisters and
brothers sat on the floor in their stockinged feet the
seven days of mourning for their mother.

"If only I had the treasure," he meditated, "Even if
I didn't have all of it, only a tiny part. . . . I could
certainly use it! Grandma Minde would stop crying.
She wouldn't scold God any more for having taken
Mother. . . . Father would not sit looking so sad.
. . . I'd fill the whole house with the treasure—piles of
silver, gold, and diamonds. They'd just have to forget
how bad they felt. . . ."

These reveries carried him off into another world, a
world of dreams. . . . He imagined that the treasure
was in his possession. Suddenly the enormous hoard
of stones and talismans had appeared. "Sholom, where
did you get all these riches?" Father asked, overwhelmed. "I can't tell you, Papa, because if I do, it
will vanish immediately!" And now Sholom was in sev-
enth heaven, for he had succeeded in rescuing his father from want. But at the same time it was too bad
that poor Mother wasn't here to enjoy it. "This is the

way it was destined," Grandma Minde said, "All her youth she suffered for the sake of her children, and now that we can really live, she is no longer with us. . . ."

His revery was interrupted by a sigh from Father. "Dear God, what shall I do?" and the little dreamer was rudely snatched back from his happy world of fantasy. Here was the dark empty world of sorrow and tears again, that world where people discussed flour for baking Sabbath loaves, money to spend in the market, and clients who would not patronize the inn, how you just couldn't make a living. . . . And, accompanying such talk, now his father sighs, "Dear God, what shall I do?"

"What do you mean, 'What shall I do'?" Uncle Pinney demanded on the last day of mourning. "You'll do what every Jew does—you'll get married!"

"Will he get married? Will Father marry again? Will we have a new mother? What will she be like?" Such thoughts buzzed in the children's minds. They looked at Father to see what his response would be. But he absolutely refused to listen.

"*Marry?* After losing such a wife, I should marry again? Is that the sort of advice I get from my own brother? You, who knew her as well as anyone?"

Tears choked him and he could not speak further. Uncle Pinney did not pursue the subject.

"It's time for the evening prayer," Uncle Pinney said, and all the mourners, Father as well as the children, rose from the ground and began to pray. Then all of the six sons, including Eli, the one who was a married man and wore a small blond beard, recited *Kaddish* [the prayer for the dead]. It was a joy to hear them, and all the relatives gazed at them with pride. The women visitors were envious. "How could you not go straight to paradise with six such *Kaddish* readers?" Bluma inquired. She was a distant relative who had a deaf-and-dumb husband. She had left her family to help Nahum out by tending to the house and looking after the children.

The children could not complain that they were being neglected. Since Mother's death, they had become very important—why, they were orphans! At times, sitting on the floor seemed to them almost a pleasure. They did not have to go to *cheder*. And they were fed tea with sugar and white bread, an unusual treat for them. And everyone felt their heads and stomachs and inquired about how they felt. All of a sudden they'd acquired stomachs! Sitting on the floor was actually fun. They shared a blanket with Father, who buried his high wrinkled brow in the Book of Job, and they watched a stream of visitors come to express their condolences. These people said the strangest things. They entered without a greeting and left without saying goodbye. They blinked in an odd way and muttered something under their breath, "Mmmm . . . mmm . . . mmm . . . Zion and Jerusalem. . . ."

For little Sholom these visitors were a treasure house of types. No two were alike, and all demand to be preserved in these pages. The first to enter was Uncle Pinney, with his two sons, Issrolik and Itzel, dressed in their very long coats. Uncle Pinney rolls up his sleeves and starts to talk, and his two sons sit one to the left of him and one to the right and listen. He is discussing a point of law: when exactly do the seven days of mourning come to an end—in the morning or in the evening? He rises, promising to take another look into his books to find out definitely. He and his sons do not say goodbye. They mutter something ending with " . . . Zion and Jerusalem . . ." and disappear. They are followed by Aunt Hannah and her daughters, who fall upon Father and begin shouting, "Enough, enough!" He must stop crying over Mother, because tears won't bring her back. Before they leave, Aunt Hannah complains that the air in the room is stifling. She takes a pinch of snuff out of her little silver box and insists that at least one window be opened because there is absolutely no air in the room. . . . Then comes Aunt Temmy's mother, a toothless woman with a trembling head; her lips smile while her eyes weep. To console everyone, she brings an important piece of news: someday we all must die! . . .

After the relatives, come the friends and acquaintances. There are all kinds: some believe in God and the other world implicitly; others are people of small faith. For instance, there is Arnold from Pidvorki, who mocks at everything. He claims there is no Providence and quotes Ecclesiastes, "A man hath no preeminence over a beast." The things Arnold says are simply dreadful! He denies all that is holy and has smooth, clever explanations for everything. He is the only one who leaves with a farewell. This is not to be wondered at, since he has no faith. But it would be interesting to know what he would do if he were suddenly to die! "When I die they can burn my carcass and throw the ashes to the four winds! It makes no difference to me," Arnold says, and receives a caustic lecture from Grandma Minde. "Let your enemies do your talking," is her advice.

Arnold does not mind. He laughs at Grandma and leaves. Immediately after him comes Yossi Fruchstein of the large teeth. He too reproaches Father for weeping; he would not have expected such behavior of him. Dodi, the son of Itzhak Avigdor, says the same thing. He swears on his word of honor that if such a misfortune were to happen to him, he would—ha, ha, ha!—make a donation to the poor box of Reb Meyer the Miracle Maker! After Dodi leaves, everyone bursts out laughing, because it's an open secret that his wife, Feiga Leah, is no bargain. . . . Thank heavens, one finally has a chance to laugh a little. Father is still studying the Book of Job, but he is no longer weeping so bitterly, nor does he become angry when Uncle Pinney mentions marriage. He merely sighs, "What's to be done with the children?"

"The children?" Uncle Pinney repeats, smoothing his beard, "the elder ones must continue to study here, and the little ones can be sent to their grandparents in Boguslav."

He is talking about Grandfather Moshe Yossi and Grandmother Gittel, Mother's parents, whom the children have never seen. All they know is that somewhere, very very far from here, in a city called Boguslav, they have very wealthy grandparents. . . . So that's where they are to be sent! It doesn't sound too bad. The journey itself is something to look forward to. Besides, there will be a new city to explore. And it will be interesting to get acquainted with grandparents whom one has never seen. . . . Only one thing worries Sholom—whom does Uncle Pinney consider the elder children and whom the smaller ones? Surely, a boy who has been confirmed—even though he is somewhat smaller than a puppy—must be considered one of the older ones. The problem worries him so much that he gradually thinks less and less about Mother, for whom he has to say *Kaddish* every morning and evening. He pays less attention to Father, who is continuously sighing and groaning, and he begins to forget about the treasure. A new idea has monopolized his thoughts: the journey to the strange city of Boguslav and Grandfather Moshe Yossi and Grandmother Gittel, who are said to be so rich—so immensely rich.

37 On the Banks of the Dnieper

THE JOURNEY TO BOGUSLAV.   THE CHILDREN TAKE THEIR
FINAL LEAVE OF GRANDMA MINDE.   SHIMON WOLF, THE
TACITURN COACHMAN.   WAITING FOR THE FERRY.   SUNSET
ON THE RIVERBANK.   THE URGE TO PRAY.

One day, toward the end of the summer, just before the Fearful Days, a wagon drove up to the house and the youngest children were loaded into it—two girls and four boys, Sholom among them. They were provided with two changes of shirts, provisions for a couple of days, a letter to Grandfather Moshe Yossi and Grandmother Gittel, and endless warnings to take care when they crossed the River Dnieper on the ferry.

Imagine, they were going to cross the Dnieper, and on a ferry! Not one of them had ever seen a ferry. They hadn't the slightest idea what one was like, but they gathered that it belonged among the good things of this world. Mother's death had been forgotten; they had forgotten everything except the Dnieper, the ferry, and the trip that lay ahead of them. But they were not allowed to forget Mother for long. Grandma Minde reminded them, over and over again, not to forget to say *Kaddish*. She patted them with her cold slippery hands, kissed them on their cheeks, and said goodbye to them for ever, since God alone knew whether she would live to see them again. . . . And it happened as her heart had foreseen. When the children returned from Boguslav, they found that Grandma Minde had joined their mother. Their graves were side by side, and Father was saying *Kaddish* for his mother, while his children prayed for theirs. . . . It was the year of the cholera— a year of continuous *Kaddish*-saying. The whole congregation was saying *Kaddish*.

How different people are! Meyer Velvel, the coachman who had brought the children from Voronko to Pereyaslov, was lively, merry, and talkative, but the new coachman, Shimon Wolf, was sullen, sleepy, and taciturn. You could fire a rifle at him or shoot at him with a cannon, but still no word passed his lips with the exception of an occasional, "Get into the wagon!" or "Get out of the wagon!" The children were absolutely dying to learn when they would reach the Dnieper, when they would cross on the ferry, what a ferry was like. . . . But what can be done when a man simply won't talk? He sat on the coach box like a huge feathery owl; he lashed his horses, smacked his thick lips, and from time to time called out, "Hey, you pox—a pox on you!" or "Hey, you plague—a plague on you!" Or else he would mutter to himself and hum something in a thin soft voice; that was when he was reciting the Psalms from memory.

And just as there are all kinds of people, so there are all kinds of horses. Shimon Wolf's horses were amazingly similar to their master; like him they were also slow and sleepy. And they had a habit of sneezing. They sneezed throughout the day, throughout the journey. They sneezed and snorted and swished their tails and crept at a snail's pace. It seemed as if they had been creeping for ages. Heaven only knew when they would arrive at some human habitation. . . .

Sky and earth and sand. Endless sand. And just for good measure the horses suddenly stopped in the middle of the road. Shimon Wolf crawled out of his seat and sang in his thin voice, "Blessed are they that put their trust in Him. . . ." Then he turned to the children, "Get out of the wagon!" The children obediently climbed out. What had happened? Nothing much. The road was so sandy that it was difficult for the horses to pull, so it was necessary to walk a bit. Well, that was not so bad. If they had to walk, walk they would. It was even more fun on foot! But the youngest orphan, the little one-year-old, did not want to be left alone in the wagon, and she cried. She had to be carried, and that was not so easy. Fortunately, it was not for long. The road soon became passable again, and the coachman turned to the children. "Get into the wagon!" They climbed in and stretched out their legs. They rode on and on until once again they reached a stretch of sand. Again, "Get out of the wagon!" and, again, "Get into the wagon!"

But what was that gleaming in the distance? What was that shining like glass, glistening in the sun with silvery hues and shimmering in front of one's eyes? Could that be the Dnieper? The children could hardly sit still in the wagon. As if out of spite, the wagon crept slowly, endlessly, and before they reached the water, they had to cross sand and more sand, thick yellow sand, knee-deep. Slowly, step by step, the horses crawled with difficulty, slowly pulling their legs out of the sand, while the wagon groaned.

Nearer and nearer came the Dnieper, with all its breadth and beauty. Yes, it was the river! It gleamed, it glittered in the sun, and it smiled to the young travelers who had come to greet the ancient Dnieper for the first time, "Hello, Grandpa, how are you?"

On the banks of the river, tall green rushes, yellow in places, spread their long sharp leaves, which were reflected in the water and contributed a peculiar charm to the river. There was silence all about.

The river spread far and wide, like an ocean, in all

directions. Its waters ran silently on. Where? Hush, it was a secret! The blue sky looked down from its great height and mirrored itself in the water with the sun that had not yet set. The sky was clean; the water, clean; and the sand and air as well. Silence. Spaciousness, divine spaciousness. One recalled the words of the psalmist, "The large place of the Lord. . . ."

Frrr! . . . That was a bird flying out of the rushes with a cry. It cut through the air like an arrow, cleft the still, clear air, and flew in zigzags, far, far away. Then, apparently thinking better of it, it returned in zigzags and again disappeared among the yellowish-green rushes. One wanted passionately to fly from the wagon like that bird and wing over the waters, or, at least, to strip, jump into the river, and swim far, far away. . . .

"Get out of the wagon!" commanded Shimon Wolf, climbing out himself. He cupped his mouth with both hands, threw back his head, and emitted a strange hollow cry which sounded as if it came from a broken keg:

"Fe-e-e-erry! Fe-e-e-erry!"

Apparently, the ferry was a living creature which inhabited the other bank of the river and would come only when one called it. The youngsters crawled out of the wagon and stretched their stiff limbs. They cupped their hands like the coachman, threw back their heads, and shouted in their thin young voices:

"Fe-e-e-erry! Fe-e-e-erry!"

Suddenly they burst into gales of laughter. Why were they laughing? They did not know why themselves, but it was probably because they were young and healthy and happy—because they were standing on the banks of the Dnieper—and because they were soon to cross the river on a ferry. What joy! But then the sun began to take its leave. With its final, pure, strong rays it was reflected in the silvery waters of the river. All laughter ceased; all desire to laugh was gone. It was too quiet there on the shores of the Dnieper. It was a holy silence. The air had become a little cooler, and a peculiar smell rose from the water. The river murmured and hummed and ran. Then the coachman tied his kerchief about his waist, and stuck his whip into this makeshift belt, and placed himself facing the east. He shut his eyes, like the pious Jew that he was, and started swaying and intoning the evening prayer in his thin voice. In the open air, beneath the many-colored sky, on the banks of the beautiful, odorous Dnieper, Shimon Wolf's prayer merged with the humming and murmuring of the water and inspired the happy young voyagers with a new mood. They too felt like praying. This was, we must admit, their first voluntary, unexacted prayer—there, under the open sky, close to God. . . . They skipped the beginning (that's a trifle—on the road, one is permitted to omit the beginning) and, starting right from "Blessed are they that dwell in Thy house," singing loudly and tunefully, they began the Eighteen Benedictions. Facing the east, their eyes shut, they swayed like the coachman. "God the great, the mighty, and the stern. . . ." For the first time one really understood the truth of these words—there, in the twilight, beneath the broad heavens, on the banks of the

Dnieper. It felt so good to pray, so sweet, so easy, as
never before. . . .

38   On the Ferry

THE FERRY.   AN UNEXPECTED ENCOUNTER BETWEEN JACOB
AND ESAU IN THE DARKNESS OF THE NIGHT.   OLD FRIENDS
RECOGNIZE ONE ANOTHER AND PART SILENTLY.

The little orphan travelers were not yet through with
their prayer when, in the distance, upon the glittering
river, they saw a dark ball which was turning all colors
beneath the rays of the sun. The ball gradually increased in size; it gleamed; it disappeared for a while
and then appeared again. Then they heard a strange
noise, a rumble and the screeching of wheels and the
squeaking of ropes. Quickly they finished the Eighteen
Benedictions and ran to the river's edge. There they
noticed for the first time a thick cable attached to a post
on their side of the riverbank and reaching clear across
the Dnieper. The growing ball took the form of a shape-
less wooden monster; for a while it looked like a house
which was swimming on the water. In the monster's
mouth was a revolving wheel by means of which the
creature moved over the river, slowly but surely, and

gradually approached the shore. When it came closer, it became clear that it was, after all, neither a monster nor a house, but a kind of boat, a barge or a raft. On it stood carts, horses, and people. Apparently this was the ferry which the children were awaiting so impatiently, and on which they were soon to cross the Dnieper. Now their hearts felt lighter. Now they could sit down on the sand for a while and wait for the ferry to reach the beach, for it approached so slowly that it scarcely seemed to move. Indeed, the sun was much swifter than the ferry. . . . The sun had already reached the horizon; gradually it descended, as if going downhill, and, as it sank, disappeared beyond the river, leaving a broad red streak behind it. The little breeze became sharper. The children settled on the sand, and the eldest boy held the smallest child in his arms; the baby slept.

The ferry arrived. One by one, slowly and silently, the people left the boat with their carts and horses. Shimon Wolf clambered out of the wagon without uttering a single word—it seemed as if everyone had made a vow of silence. He drove the wagon on to the ferry, without even cursing the horses as usual; then he signaled to the little travelers to come on board. In another minute, the vessel, navigated by a man who pulled on the thick cable with all his might, quietly sailed off— so quietly that you did not even feel it move. The river, not the ferry, seemed to be moving—as if the Dnieper was retreating from them.

Now, for the first time, one really saw how large the Dnieper was, how broad and beautiful. One sailed on and on, and still the opposite shore was distant. The sun had set long ago behind the river, and the moon had come out. At first the moon was red; then it turned white—pure white, almost silvery. One by one the stars lit up the deep sky like Sabbath candles. In the dusk, the Dnieper changed its color; the river looked as if it had swathed itself in a dark cloak, and it breathed a fresh coolness, a smooth light coolness. One's head filled with a thousand thoughts—thoughts of the night, the sky, the stars which were mirrored in the still waters, each little star a human soul. . . . And new longings awoke in little Sholom's heart, emotions he had not known before. He thought of his mother, little Haya Esther, in her dark lonely grave, forgotten and forsaken by her children, who were traveling to distant places. He thought of his father, prematurely old and wrinkled. He thought of the wonderful journey the orphans were making to the end of the world. . . . And he thought how wonderful it was that it took only one unsightly peasant boy to steer the ferry. The boy pulled the cable with one hand; the wheel revolved, and the ferry moved.

Sholom was anxious to have a better look at the peasant; he wanted to watch him work the cable and navigate. He came closer to the ferryman, who proved to be a very young boy dressed in a gray peasant overcoat, big boots, and a fur cap. He kept bearing down on the thick cable. Sholom watched the peasant ferryman work with all his might; he moved his shoulders up and down until it seemed one could hear his bones creak. "Esau," Sholom thought, "Esau. . . . Only a peasant can do such work—a Jew, never. For how could a Jew perform such coarse labor? 'Thou shalt serve thy brother,' said

Isaac to Esau. . . . How lucky that I'm descended from Jacob and not from Esau!"

He felt very sorry for the poor young peasant, the descendant of Esau. He was so young, much too young for such work. . . . Sholom peered closer into his face and jumped back. The face looked familiar. Familiar eyes. Unabashed, he came still closer to the peasant—but the lad was not a peasant! He was a very young boy with a coarsened sunburnt face and dark rough hands. His eyes were Jewish, but his hands were peasant's hands. . . . Again he remembered Genesis, ". . . but the hands are the hands of Esau. . . ." Why did the ferryman seem so familiar to him? Where had he seen him before?

Sholom plumbed his memory and suddenly recalled Berl the Widow's Son, a dark boy with large teeth, one of his Voronko friends. Could this be he? Impossible, he was simply imagining it! But yet, it must be Berl! . . . Sensing himself watched, the lad pulled his cap lower down, but glanced slyly to see who was looking at him so intently. The eyes of the two boys met in the darkness of the night, and they recognized one another.

This unexpected meeting evoked a host of thoughts. Had Berl become a peasant, a peasant Jew? Sholom recollected that even in those days it had been said that Berl was a convert—no wonder he had been nicknamed "The *Goy*". . . . Should he speak to Berl, identify himself? Something held Sholom back. He felt strange, distant, cold—and at the same time he felt pity—pity for a Jew who had turned peasant. Why had he done it? So that he could dress in a gray overcoat, a large shaggy hat, and become a ferryman's apprentice? But the apprentice paid no heed to him; he did not even turn around. Apparently he could not look his old friend straight in the eye. Berl gazed into the water as if he had noticed something interesting there; he retreated deeper into his gray coat and pulled his hat further down over his eyes. Then he spat on the palms of his hands and returned to his work with renewed zeal. He pulled down on the cable with all his strength, and the cable creaked, the wheel revolved, the ferry glided farther and farther on. . . . They had arrived!

"Get into the wagon!" ordered the taciturn coachman after he had driven the wagon and horses off the ferry. Then he lashed the horses with his whip, giving them their usual dose of "pox" and "plague," and they were off, leaving behind the Dnieper, the ferry, and the ferryman's apprentice, who slowly disappeared into the darkness of night.

39 In the Boguslav Market Place

BOGUSLAV DURING A FAIR.   WHICH IS THEIR GRANDFATHER?
A PIOUS JEW TAKES THEM UNDER HIS WING.

When the young orphans arrived in Boguslav, tired, sleepy, and hungry, it was already day. The sun was rising, clear, brilliant, and warm, from the other side of the forest. On the outskirts of the town, their wagon passed a huge cemetery full of broken gravestones with worn-out inscriptions. Judging by the size of the cemetery, it seemed that Boguslav must be a metropolis.

After they passed the graveyard, they came to a large market place full of shops and stalls and pushcarts. It made a colorful picture—a confusion of strange creatures, human and animal, carts and wagons, halters and yokes, utensils of every sort, and various foodstuffs, all thrown together indiscriminately. Peasants were wandering about, strolling with their wives and children. Gypsies loitered here and there. Horses neighed, cows mooed, pigs squealed . . . and above all this din, one heard the voices of the Jews. There were Jews of all kinds: Jews marketing furs, Jews selling hats, Jews dealing in cloth, Jews selling bread and cakes and buns and cider, and anything else you could think of. . . . And the Jewish women! They elbowed their way through the confusion, carrying baskets, selling chickens and fried fish and pickled apples and buttons and thread. The noise was enormous. Everyone was talking, every tongue was wagging. Beggars, lame and blind, sat on the ground lamenting their fate, and animals echoed them loudly, till one thought one would go deaf. Dust swirled in thick clouds, till it concealed the sun; strange odors blended, till one felt suffocated. . . . The young visitors had picked a fine moment to enter Boguslav— the busiest day of the year, market day.

The coachman just managed to squeeze his wagon through the market place. As was his custom, he called

down a hundred plagues upon the city and its fair, and
then they drove into the town proper, which bore a
striking resemblance to the graveyard: the houses were
as dilapidated as the tombstones; here and there were a
few new buildings which looked very peculiar in the
motley group, like wealthy relatives at a poor man's
wedding. And now the real confusion began. Shimon
Wolf knew he had been instructed to bring the children
to their grandparents. He had been told their names,
but—what the devil!—they had clean slipped his mind!
He swore that, as true as he was alive, he had remembered them the whole journey, but the moment they
had entered the market place, the names had flown out
of his head. "A plague on him!" (On whom, he did not
specify.)

Meanwhile, a Jew approached their wagon, then another Jew, and yet another. Then two other Jews joined
them, followed by three more Jews, and women of all
kinds—women with baskets and women without baskets. There was a fearful confusion. Everyone was talking at once, telling each other about the extraordinary
event: a coachman had brought some children.

"Where from?"

"From the other side of the Dnieper."

"You mean from Rezhishchev?"

"Why from Rezhishchev? Why not from Kanev?"

"No, not Rezhishchev or Kanev, but from Pereyaslov!"

"Where to?"

"Can't you see for yourself? Not to Yehupetz, but to
Boguslav!"

"To whom?"

"An intelligent question! If we knew, we wouldn't ask you!"

"Quiet, everyone! I have an idea. Ask the children what their grandfather is named—they must know."

"That's right! Let me, I'll ask them!" said a Jew who sold rolls. He pushed his way through the crowd. He was wearing a cap with a broken visor, and he shoved the people aside with both his elbows.

"Children, what's your grandfather called?"

Because of the noise and the confusion, the children had become confused. But they still remembered that their grandfather's name was Moshe Yossi. Besides, they had with them a letter from their father to their grandfather.

The Jew started to examine the letter from all sides and found it addressed in the proper manner: "To my dear and honored father-in-law, the famous nobleman, the sage and God-fearing Hasid, Moshe Yossi."

Now that it had been discovered that their grandfather was Moshe Yossi, it only remained to determine *which* Moshe Yossi, for there were several. There was Moshe Yossi the carpenter, Moshe Yossi the tinsmith, Moshe Yossi the husband of Leah Dvossi, and Moshe Yossi from the village of Hamarnia. . . . Take your choice!

"Quiet, everyone! Children, tell me what your father is called," another Jew said, a man who wore his *talith katan* over his clothes—apparently a very pious Jew. The children replied that Father was called Nahum. When the new Jew heard this, he pushed everyone aside and put the children through a real cross examination.

"You say your father's name is Nahum? Is he called Rabinowitz?"

"Yes, Rabinowitz."

"And your mother was called Haya Esther?"

"Yes, Haya Esther."

"And she died?"

"Yes, she died."

"Of the cholera?"

"The cholera."

"Well, why didn't you say so in the first place!" The pious man turned to the rest of the public, his face shining.

"In that event, *I'm* the man you should have asked for! I can tell you all about them. Their grandfather is Moshe Yossi Hamarnik. Their grandmother is Gittel. Their grandfather knows that his daughter, Haya Esther, died of cholera, but their grandmother doesn't. No one wants to break the dreadful news to her because she's an old woman and a cripple in the bargain. . . ."

The pious man turned to the children, his face still shining.

"Climb out of the wagon, children! I'll show you where your grandfather lives. It's impossible to drive straight up to the house because the path is too narrow. Or maybe you could drive in from the other side? But no, you couldn't possibly turn the wagon around there. . . . Mottel, what do you think, could they turn the wagon around there?"

The last sentence was addressed to a young man with a crooked nose. Mottel pushed his cap back.

"Why couldn't they?"

"Why? Because! Have you forgotten that Hershke, the son of Itzie Liabess, is building a stable there?"

Mottel did not move an eyelash. He asked, "And what if he is building a stable there? What of it?"

"What do you mean, 'What of it'? He has stacked all the lumber there!"

"Lumber? May he use it in good health!"

The pious man remained for a moment staring at Mottel open-mouthed; then he turned, spat, and, grasping one of the children by the hand, said, "Let's go, children. I'll take you there. We've got to walk." The pious man with the shining face moved off with the young travelers, to the home of Grandfather Moshe Yossi and Grandmother Gittel, and the fringes of his ritual garments swung around his knees.

40 A Fine Welcome

CRIPPLED GRANDMOTHER GITTEL.   THE RICH GRANDFATHER.
UNCLE ITZIE AND AUNTIE SOSSIE.

The little Pereyaslov orphans were fully justified in expecting that Grandfather Moshe Yossi's home would be a palace and their grandfather a patriarch in a silken coat. Hadn't they been told he was rich, oh so immensely rich? . . .

The pious Jew with the shining face finally brought them to a very ordinary little house, though it did have a glass-covered porch. The pious Jew said, "That's where your grandfather lives," and disappeared. Apparently he did not wish to be present at the reception. The children marched through the glass entrance, opened the door, and found themselves in a dark dreary room smelling of damp sheepskins. Opposite the door, they saw, lying on a wooden bed, a person who was hardly a person, a creature that was hardly a creature—something the shape of a woman but with weirdly twisted arms and withered legs. Their first impulse was to turn and run, but the creature had caught sight of them and, after examining them intently with her red, shining eyes, asked in a lovely soft voice, "Who are you, children?" Recognizing something dear and familiar in that voice, they replied, "Good morning! We come from Pereyaslov."

When the old woman heard the word "Pereyaslov" and saw a group of children with a baby less than a year old among them, she immediately sensed what had happened, and, twisting her crooked hands, she cried loudly, "These are Haya Esther's children! My Haya Esther is dead!" and she began to beat her head with her hands. "Moshe Yossi, Moshe Yossi, where are you? Come here, Moshe Yossi!"

Out of a small side chamber, an old man, clad in a prayer shawl and phylacteries, came running. He had a hairy, heavy face, a broad, bulbous nose, and remarkably thick eyebrows. He was dressed in rags and on his feet were worn-out slippers. Could this be Grandfather Moshe Yossi, who was rich, oh so immensely rich?

The first thing Grandfather did was to start shouting at the children, scolding them and waving his hands. As he had been interrupted in the middle of a prayer, he could express himself only in monosyllabic sounds and in the Holy Tongue. "*Ee . . . o . . . nu!* Criminals! Murderers!" Then he turned to the old woman, speaking to her also in Hebrew, his voice shaking, "*Ee . . . o . . . nu!* I know . . . my daughter . . . The Lord gave and the Lord hath taken away! . . ."

This meant that he knew of his daughter's death, and that God, Who had given her to them, had taken her back. . . . But this did not console the old woman. She continued to sob, and to beat her head with her hands and wail, "Haya Esther! My Haya Esther is dead!" till more people came running. The first to appear was an odd-looking man with exceedingly long curly earlocks, such as the children had never seen in Pereyaslov. He was their mother's only brother, Uncle Itzie. Next, a woman with a flaming face, her sleeves rolled up and a wooden spoon in her hands, rushed in evidently straight from the kitchen. This was his wife, Auntie Sossie. With her came a little girl. She was very shy and pretty, and had pink cheeks and a tiny rosebud mouth; her name was Hava Liba. Then a host of other men and women appeared—in fact, all the neighbors— and everyone commenced to talk simultaneously, trying to console Grandmother Gittel. Her daughter was dead, could tears bring her back? That which the earth had covered was buried forever. . . . After this they started to scold the young guests for descending on the house without warning. How could one break such news to a mother in such an abrupt fashion? . . . Although the heavens bore witness to the fact that the children had not breathed a single word!

In the meantime, Grandfather had removed his prayer shawl and phylacteries, and now took his turn in upbraiding his grandchildren. Why hadn't they come to him first? If they had had any sense, they would have seen him and talked it over with him carefully. He would have spoken to Grandmother tactfully, prepared her gradually for the shock—not let her know the way they had, like a thunderbolt! That's how savages behaved, not civilized people!

But this was too much for Grandmother Gittel, and although the blow had been a heavy one, she turned upon Grandfather.

"What have you against the poor children, you old fool? How is it their fault? How should they know you spend the whole day lying on your sheepskins, praying? A fine welcome this is! . . . Come to me, darlings. What are your names?"

She beckoned to the children, asked each his name, patted them, kissed them, and watered them with her tears—tears which were now no longer for her poor lost daughter but for the lonely little orphans. . . . She swore she had known for a long time that her Haya Esther was dead. It had been as clear as day, for hadn't she dreamed about Haya Esther on several consecutive nights, and each time her daughter had inquired about her children and had wanted to know how devoted her mother was to them. . . .

"Give them something to eat! Moshe Yossi, why do you stand there like a statue? Can't you see for yourself, you old fool, that the poor children are hungry and exhausted? They probably haven't slept all night. Good heavens, he's still lecturing them! A fine grandfather he is! A fine welcome!"

41   Among Sheepskins

GRANDPARENTS' BUSINESS.   GRANDFATHER, THE BOOKKEEPER, AND GRANDMOTHER, THE TREASURER.   GRANDFATHER'S LEC-TURES, BOOKS, AND BENEFACTIONS.   WHAT WILL HAPPEN WHEN THE MESSIAH COMES?   RELIGIOUS ECSTASY.

The first thing Grandfather Moshe Yossi did, after his grandchildren had eaten, was to examine their minds.

The examination took place in his special little room, which no stranger was allowed to enter. To enter it was neither permitted nor was it easy. This room was only slightly larger than a hen coop, and two people could just about squeeze into it. Here, besides Grandfather and his books (the whole of the Talmud, the Law-makers, and Kabbalistic treatises), were silver spoons, trays, spice holders, lamps, candelabra, copper bowls, samovars, Jewish caftans, peasants' beads, peasants' coats, and sheepskins—especially sheepskins. There were sheepskins without end!

It was, in fact, a sort of pawnshop, for many years energetically run by Grandmother Gittel despite the fact that she was paralyzed and bedridden. She kept the cash box under her pillow and would let no one near it. But it was Grandfather who took care of the pledges. He received the articles and later returned them. It would have required the brains of a genius to remember what belonged to whom, and perhaps Grandfather did have such a brain, but he dared not rely on it. . . . And so he devised a method all his own. On each pledge he sewed a piece of paper upon which he wrote in Hebrew, "This coat belongs to Berl the Jew," or, "This sheepskin is Ivan the Peasant's," or, "These are the beads of Eudoxia the Peasant Woman." But suppose Berl came to claim his coat and received a coat belonging to another Berl? Grandfather insured himself against this contingency by carrying out the coats of both Berls and asking the man to identify his own. No Jew would deceive him and claim the coat of another. But it was not so simple when it was a peasant who was involved. Still, there was a solution for that, too; a learned Jew can find a solution for anything. Grandfather would require Ivan to name some identifying mark. Every peasant knew his sheepskin inside out, and there was never an article without some idiosyncrasy of its own. Yet, despite all these precautions, Grandfather and Grandmother often had falling-outs over his system.

"Listen, old fool," she would ask, "when you write 'This coat belongs to Berl the Jew,' why can't you add another word: 'Berl the tongue-tied Jew'? When you write 'This sheepskin belongs to Ivan the Peasant,' give his full name, 'Ivan the Thief'! Let me know that the beads are the property of pug-nosed Eudoxia!"

But Grandfather Moshe Yossi (may he not hold my saying it against me when we meet in the next world) was an extremely stubborn man. Since that was the way *she* wanted it, it was the way *he* did *not* want it! Nor could you really blame him for that, for whoever heard of a bedridden cripple ordering her husband about and calling him "old fool" in the presence of his grand-children? One would think that he was a nobody! And he was Reb Moshe Yossi Hamarnik's who, day in and day out, night in and night out, sat studying the Torah! He was Reb Moshe Yossi Hamarnik's who observed all the fasts, and even fasted every Monday and Thursday! All week long, except for Sabbaths and holidays, he did not permit a morsel of meat to pass his lips. And was he not the first to arrive at synagogue and the last to leave? When other Jews were already fast asleep, he was just saying grace for the Sabbath meal. And Grand-mother Gittel had the temerity to scold him—but it was not for her own sake; it was for the sake of the poor orphans.

Of all the children, Grandfather took a fancy to only one—Sholom. True enough, he was a mischief-maker, but he did have a good head on his shoulders. He might even become somebody, if he could be persuaded to spend more time with Grandfather in his littered chamber, and if only he did not have the nasty habit of running off with Boguslav boys to the River Ross to watch the fishing, or into the forest to gather pears. . . .

"If your father were a sensible man," Grandfather explained, "if his head weren't stuffed with such nonsense as the Bible and the Commentaries and grammar, he'd leave you with me. Then, with God's grace, I'd make a pious Jew out of you. We might even turn you into a Hasid, a real Kabbalist. But the way things are, you'll be an absolute nobody, a loafer, a drone, a clod, a dissenter, a sinner, an unbeliever, a Sabbath-breaker, a rebel against the God of Israel! . . ."

"Moshe Yossi, do stop torturing that child!"

And Sholom would bless Grandmother Gittel for rescuing him from Grandfather's clutches. Outside, the Boguslav children would be waiting for him.

Yet there were times when he loved his grandfather and felt very close to him. Once, Sholom found him sitting on Grandmother's bed, the prayer-shawl bag under his arm. He was speaking in a whisper, haggling stubbornly, and pleading for more money, which she flatly refused to give him. He was not begging for himself, but for his poor congregation in the Hasidic synagogue, but she kept repeating, "Not another penny!" She had her own orphans to support . . . they were more to be pitied. . . .

Another time, Sholom found Grandfather in his little room, in prayer shawl and phylacteries, head thrown back, eyes shut, and, it seemed, in another world. When he finally came to, the Divine Spirit seemed to be upon him. He was whispering to himself, a strange smile on his mouth.

"Not for long shall Edom continue to rule the world! Salvation is close at hand, it is very close! Come, my child, sit down and I'll tell you about the end of the world and what will happen when the Messiah comes. . . ."

And Grandfather embraced the child and began to tell him what would happen when the Messiah came. With such enthusiasm and ecstasy and flaming colors was the Messiah's advent described that the boy could not tear his eyes from Grandfather's face, and involuntarily thought of Shmulik, his first and dearest friend. The difference was that Shmulik had spoken of treasures and sorcerers and princes and princesses—things that belonged to this world—whereas Grandfather had no use for this world and transported his grandson to another world, a higher one, where everything was pure and holy, where there were saints and angels, seraphim and cherubim sitting close to God's throne, in sweet proximity to the King of Kings himself, blessed be His name. . . . There you'd find the Shor-Habar and the Leviathan; there you'd discover that most precious ointment, Apharsemon, and that most precious sacred wine. There the saints sat immersed in study, joyfully partaking of the Divine Spirit and the Hidden Light which God concealed when He created the world and saw that humanity was unworthy. The Lord in all His glory would stand and serve the saints himself, as a father might serve his children. And out of the heavens, down to the very place where once the Great Temple stood, a new Temple would descend, cast from pure gold and inlaid with precious stones. The priests would bless the people, the Levites would sing, and King David himself would come to greet them with his lyre, "Rejoice in the Lord, O ye righteous!"

And Grandfather Moshe Yossi began to sing aloud. He snapped his fingers, his eyes were shut, his face glowed with ecstasy, and he was no longer in this world. He was far away, in another world, in a very, very different world, a world pure and holy and good. . . .

42   The Bird-Jew

AN OLD STORY.   JEWISH LIFE OF OLD AND THE NOBLES
OF THOSE DAYS.   THE TRAGEDY OF A POOR INNKEEPER.
THE MORAL.

One must not suppose that Grandfather Moshe Yossi always lived in that other, distant world, and had nothing to tell his little grandchildren about this one. He could tell a great deal about the ancient Jews, the Hasidim and the Kabbalists, and the nobility, too, and how they had treated the Jews.

His grandchildren were particularly impressed by the story of one Jewish martyr. We shall make the story short because Grandfather (may he forgive us) liked to draw things out; he would jump so much from one incident to another that, in the end, he would find himself far from the original subject and unable to return to it.

Before the time of his grandfather, the old Hamarnik —so named because Hamarnia was the name of the village where he lived and leased a mill—there lived in the same village another Jew, a certain Noah, who ran an inn. Noah was a naive, simple man, but a very pious one. He prayed day and night, and read the Psalms continuously. Perhaps he was a saint, perhaps a repentant soul—who knows? His wife ran the inn, and his share of the work was simply to pay rent at the lord's manor and to renew the lease from year to year. All his life he dreaded that someone would outbid him and buy the inn. There were many who coveted it, although he himself gained little from the business. And, burdened as he was with a large family, he could barely make ends meet.

One day, when he went to renew his lease, he found the manor full of guests. A real feast was in progress. After the feast, the noblemen prepared as usual to go hunting. The horses were ready; there was a cavalcade of coaches, carriages, and traps; there were dogs of all breeds, and hunters with hunting horns and large feathers in their hats—everything was arranged in regal fashion.

"I've come at an inopportune moment," thought Noah, "The lord won't have time to talk about the lease now." But he was mistaken. The lord left the festive board with his guests, and was just about to mount his horse when he caught sight of the Jew, shrunken and tattered, standing to one side. The lord cried merrily, "How are you, Innkeeper Jew?" Noah replied, "Thank you, Most Illustrious Sir. I have come about the lease." The lord laughed; he was a bit tipsy and in a good humor. "For how many years would you like your lease to be renewed?" Noah answered, "I'd like to have it for several years, but your rules, Most Illustrious Lord . . ." The lord interrupted him, "Very well, this time I'll let you have the inn at the same rental as before, for a term of ten years. But there is one condition —you must turn into a bird!" The Jew wondered, "How can I turn into a bird?" The lord replied, "Very simply. Climb upon the roof of this stable, and pretend you're a bird. I'll aim at you and try to hit you in the head. Understand?" The rest of the noblemen burst out laughing. The Jew also pretended to laugh. He thought, "The lord is joking. He's had a drop too much. . . ." "Well?" asked the lord. Noah thought, "What should I answer him?" Aloud, he asked, with a smile, "How long will you give me to decide?" Quite seriously, the lord replied, "A whole minute!" A minute, and no more! "The choice is up to you," he added, "either you climb upon the roof and turn into a bird, or tomorrow you'll be kicked out of the inn!" The Jew felt as if his soul were leaving his body. What was he to do? One couldn't trifle with a nobleman! . . . In the meantime, the lord had already called for a ladder—evidently he was deadly serious. Again the Jew asked, "What will happen if you hit me, God forbid?" At this the guests only laughed, and Noah remained completely bewildered, for he still did not know if the lord was joking.

But apparently the lord was in earnest, for he commanded Noah to climb the ladder at once or else abandon the inn. Noah had already turned to leave, when suddenly, thinking of his houseful of children, he begged the lord to give him a few more minutes to make his confession. The lord said, "Very well, I'll give you another minute to make your confession." One single minute! What can a Jew say in the space of one minute besides *"Shmah Yisroel . . ."*? He was already being pushed toward the ladder. So he said, *"Shmah Yisroel"* and "Blessed be the name of His glorious kingdom forever," and tears started from his eyes. He began to climb the ladder, for what else was there to do? The will of heaven . . . a houseful of children . . . apparently fated to die a martyr's death . . . perhaps God would have mercy on him and a miracle would occur . . . whatever the Lord willed, He could do. . . . Noah had great faith, for great was the faith of the Jews of long ago.

When he reached the roof, though still weeping and whispering the prayer, he had not yet despaired that God might have mercy on him, for whatever the Almighty willed, He could do. . . . Meanwhile, the lord was becoming impatient. He ordered the Jew to stand up straight, so Noah stood up straight. Then he told him to bend over, and Noah bent over—to fling his arms wide open, and Noah opened them wide—to turn into a bird . . . and Noah turned into a bird! Whether the lord had meant it as a joke or not, we do not know, but the Almighty caused it to happen. The lord fired and hit Noah in the forehead. He fell like a pierced bird and rolled down from the roof.

That very day, he was laid to rest in the Jewish burial ground. But the lord kept his word, and for ten years he did not interfere with the innkeeper's widow, despite the fact that the rental kept rising in value. Such were the lords of long ago!

Breathtaking stories of ancient Jews and noblemen Grandfather knew by the dozen, and the children would have listened to all of them with delight if Grandfather had not had the unpleasant habit of squeezing a moral out of each tale: one had to be a pious Jew and have faith in God. . . . The moral would be followed by a lecture, and then he would start upbraiding the children for heeding the Spirit of Evil, for having no desire to pray, study, and serve God, and for wanting only to fish night and day, pick pears, and get into mischief with worthless, empty-headed Boguslav boys. . . .

43 Among Street Urchins

ROSS, THE BOGUSLAV RIVER.   THE FOREST OF BOGUSLAV.
AVREMEL, THE SWIMMING TEACHER.   THE OLD SYNAGOGUE.

Who knows what attracted the children most, once they
were liberated from Grandfather's dark little room—
the River Ross, the Boguslav forest, or the Old Synagogue? It is hard to say which they found the most en-
trancing.

On the banks of the River Ross, there's life, joy, and
excitement. Coachmen water their horses. Water carri-
ers fill their barrels. Barefoot women and girls, their
pink calves showing beneath their skirts, wash clothes,
rinsing them and beating them with washing-beetles
until they splash all about. Dozens of children bathe,
swim, and fish. . . . They undress behind the rocks,
jump into the river, and yell at the tops of their voices,
"Watch me swim! . . . Watch me float! . . . Look at
me, how I tread water! . . . Watch me dive! . . .
Look at the bubbles I'm blowing! . . ." Everyone
shouts, performs some trick; everyone shows off. The
Pereyaslov orphans watch enviously. A boy comes up to
them. He is stark naked, and his name is Avremel.
Avremel is as black as a Tartar, he has bulging eyes,
his face is flat as a board, and his nose looks like a kid-
ney bean.

"What's your name?"

"Sholom."

"Know how to swim?"

"No."

"Why are you standing there? Come, I'll teach you!"

Do you understand? *Teach*—and not *show*, which is quite another matter!

The forest has other, though equal, charms for them. The Boguslav forest is rich in pears. It is true, they are as hard as stones and as sour as vinegar, but they are pears all the same! Besides, they are free of charge and you can pick as many as you like. But you've got to know how to get at them. Wild pears grow high. You have to climb the tree and shake it with all your might, or else the pears won't fall. In this forest there are nuts, too— hazel nuts which ripen late and are covered with a very bitter shell. They are still without any kernels; some day, they'll be full grown, but, for the present, who cares? They are nuts, aren't they, and you can fill your pockets with them. Best of all, you can gather them yourself, although you must know how. Avremel knows. Avremel knows everything. He is good-natured and kindhearted, a boy without venom. The only thing wrong with him is his poverty. His mother is an impoverished widow who works as a cook for the Yampolskis. When Uncle Itzie discovered this friendship, he immediately informed Grandmother Gittel about it, in secret. Grandmother called her grandson Sholom to her bed, took a pear from under the pillow, and gave it to him, after repeating several times that he was strictly forbidden to associate with boys like Avremel because,

207

if Grandfather found out that his grandsons associated with "such" boys, there would be a terrible fuss.

It was easy for them to say, "Don't associate with the boy," but he couldn't avoid seeing Avremel at least twice a day—in the morning and at night, when they both recited *Kaddish* in the synagogue. Avremel was also an orphan, and he also had to recite *Kaddish* for his father. Such a lot of people recited *Kaddish* in the syngogue, and everyone recited it in the place of honor, at the east wall. When the grandchildren of Moshe Yossi Hamarnik came to the Old Synagogue for the first time, their grandfather immediately took them to the beadle, whom he sternly enjoined to have the children recite *Kaddish* at the altar because they came from an excellent family. The beadle, an old man with a crooked spine and red, trachomatous eyes, listened to Grandfather respectfully, without uttering a single word. He stuffed a good portion of snuff up his nostrils, shook his fingers, tapped the snuffbox cover with his nail, and, offering it to Grandfather, silently invited him to a pinch of snuff. This evidently signified, "It's good you told me the children come from an excellent family. You can be sure I'll treat them like the apple of my eye. So what more can I say?"

The Old Synagogue seemed perfectly magnificent to the little Pereyaslov orphans. They had seen many synagogues and prayer houses in their little native village and in the big city of Pereyaslov, but the Old Synagogue of Boguslav had a charm and magic of its own. They were so enchanted with its antique beauty that they felt they had been born and raised beside it. Its large stained-glass windows, its ancient ark carved in the shape of the Temple and resting on two large lions' heads, the gorgeous painting indicating the direction of the east and depicting small and large beasts, the black cupboards, old and tall, all stuffed with ancient volumes, the tall oaken pulpits, so heavy that no one could budge them, and even the ancient rusted copper washbasin where the old people washed their hands as they entered, and out of which the children drew water simply for the fun of it—all these things seemed to them exceptional, holy, and awe-inspiring. Every inch of the building was embellished with the beauty and sanctity of the past. It seemed to them like an ancient temple, a glorious remnant of former glory—a fragment of the Temple of Solomon.

44 Among the Hasidim

THE FEARFUL DAYS IN THE OLD SYNAGOGUE.   GRANDMOTHER
GITTEL PERFORMS THE EXPIATORY SACRIFICE OF KAPAROTH.
GRANDFATHER'S BLESSING.

If the Old Synagogue appeared so magnificent to the Pereyaslov orphans on ordinary days, on the Fearful Days—*Rosh Hashonah* and *Yom Kippur*—it became transformed into a real Temple. Never had they seen so many Jews in one place and never had they witnessed such devotions. All types of Hasidim congregated here. They prayed frenziedly, clapped their hands, snapped their fingers, and sang strange melodies. Sometimes they started to howl until, being quite spent, they had only enough voice left to hum and mumble; then they would suddenly freeze in a state of ecstasy until once again they would break out loudly singing with renewed vigor.

For the Pereyaslov orphans this sort of worship was a real spectacle and novelty. But the greatest treat was to see Grandfather Moshe Yossi outdo them all with his style of praying. He was not a zealot; he was simply a peculiar kind of Hasid with eccentricities and mannerisms of his own. On Sabbaths and holidays, he would remain in the synagogue long after the others had gone. Uncle Itzie, who lived in the other half of the house, would already be at his supper, from which wafted the aroma of *gefilte* fish and other holiday delicacies. The children's mouths would water, their empty stomachs would contract, but Grandfather was still in the synagogue, praying, singing, and humming.

Once in a while, Grandmother Gittel would stealthily slip the youngsters a piece of cake to still their hunger and say, with a smile, "It'll take you a long time to forget the days you spent among madmen."

In the meantime, Uncle Itzie, who had finished eating and saying the after-meal grace, would thrust his head into the doorway. "Hasn't Father returned yet? Ha, ha, ha!" Wasn't it bad enough that he had already eaten—did he also have to mock them? But at last, long-awaited Grandfather would arrive. He would burst through the door, dragging his coat along the floor, its sleeves flapping emptily, and with a loud *"Gut Yom Tov!"* would immediately start shouting grace so loudly that it must have been heard throughout the street.

"For the sake of the children, for the sake of the poor orphans, can't you forget your freakishness this once and make it short?" Grandmother would plead. All in vain —he did not even hear her. He was still bewitched and soaring in distant spheres. Finally, he sat down at the table. Gently swaying, he ate with his right hand; with his left, he thumbed an old book into which he peeked with one eye; with the other eye, he glanced at his grandchildren, sighing deeply from time to time.

His sighs were directed at the orphans, whose souls were concerned with the world of the flesh, who enjoyed eating, and who delivered themselves bodily to the Spirit of Evil and all his passions. . . . After supper, his sighs were replaced by rebukes. He delivered a long lecture to each one in turn. He must have been anxious that all the delicious dishes which had been concocted by Grandmother Gittel while she was in bed —the fresh bread, the *gefilte* fish, and the sweet parsnips —should stick in their throats!

That was on *Rosh Hashonah.* On *Yom Kippur* it was better still. In Grandfather's home this holy day was distinguished by two peculiar ceremonies which made a lasting impression on the orphans. The first was the ceremony of *Kaparoth,* the expiatory sacrifice conducted the night before the holiday. At home this custom was also observed, but in Boguslav it was performed differently. It was Grandmother Gittel's responsibility. Sitting up in bed, she called the children and gave each one his fowl—roosters to the boys and hens to the girls. She opened her large prayer book and, with her crooked finger, pointed to the prayer "Children of Men." The older children repeated the prayer themselves, but to the little ones she read it aloud, making them repeat it word for word, with the correct litany: "Children of men such as sit in darkness and in the shadow of death, being bound in affliction and iron. . . ." And all the while she wept copious tears, as one weeps for the dead. When the littlest orphan's turn came—the baby girl hardly more than a year old —Grandmother almost fainted with emotion. Watching her cry, the children also burst into tears, and, finally, the grownups joined in. There was loud sobbing and wailing throughout the house. The children wept more during this rite than on that bitter Sabbath when their mother lay on the floor covered with black.

The other ceremony took place on the morning of the next day, after they returned from the Old Synagogue, where they had received cakes from the chief trustee. On the previous day, right after the *Kaparoth* ceremony, Grandfather had told them that the next morning, after prayers, they were to come to him for a blessing.

That day, Grandfather was in a particularly solemn mood. He was dressed very festively. Over his old satin coat, cracked along the seams, he wore a peculiar overcoat made of some stiff rustling cloth which is now unobtainable. On his head he wore a tall fur hat, decorated with numerous squirrel's tails, and around his neck was a broad snow-white collar with two sharp ends. He was girdled with a broad belt with long knotted fringes. His very broad beard and thick eyebrows did not look as stern as usual; his face seemed softer, more friendly and charitable.

"Come closer, children, I want to bless you!" he called solemnly to the orphans, leading them into his dark, small room, full of sheepskins. He laid both his hands, lost in the sleeves of his satin coat, upon each little head in turn. He shut his eyes, threw his head back, softly whispered something, and sighed deeply. When he was finished, the children looked at his face and saw that his eyes were red and glistening, his eyelashes moist, and his beard wet, wet with tears.

45 The Feast of Tabernacles

A COMMUNAL TABERNACLE.   GRANDFATHER PRAYS, AND THE
CHILDREN STARVE.   A SPECTACLE.   THE CHILDREN HATE
THEIR UNCLE.

The days of tears did not, however, last long. *Yom Kippur* passed, and with it the tears. There began the days of rejoicing and happiness, *Succoth,* the Feast of Tabernacles.

The first stave of Grandfather's tabernacle was raised on the evening following *Yom Kippur*. Uncle Itzie built the booth with the help of the orphans, but it was Grandfather who gave the commands, like an experienced architect. "This goes here! . . . That goes there! . . . This will do! . . . That won't do! . . ." Oddly enough, Grandfather and Uncle Itzie were not on speaking terms. They were angry with each other, and this caused Grandmother no end of grief. An only son, the only heir "in a hundred and twenty years," and he didn't speak to his own father! Who ever heard of such a thing?

In this communal tabernacle, two large tables were prepared, one for Grandfather and one for Uncle. On each table there were wine for the blessing, bread, and candles, arranged separately. Aunt Sossie blessed the candles at her table, and Grandmother Gittel (who was carried in on her bed) blessed hers. Then Uncle came from the synagogue. He had to wait for Grandfather to arrive and be the first to pronounce grace. One could not be rude to one's father, for it is written: "Honor thy father and mother. . . ." From time to time, Uncle Itzie would leave the house to peek into the tabernacle, each time with a different excuse. "Isn't he here yet? . . . This time the Hasidim are later than usual! . . . Hmmm! The candles are burning out, and we'll have to eat in the dark. . . ." The children secretly gloated over their uncle's discomfort, for he was a harsh, heartless man—it wouldn't hurt him to experience the sensation of hunger!

But at last Grandfather comes, dressed in his holiday

coat and flourishing the thick prayer book of Rabbi Jacob Emden. Sonorously he greets them and starts reciting the prayer "*Ushpizin.*" He chants and chants and chants. . . . As if out of spite, from the kitchen come delicious aromas of fish, peppered stuffing, and fresh crisp bread, which tickle the palate and seem to tease, "If you'd dip us into hot fish-sauce, you'd taste something heavenly!" And Grandfather is still chanting. The candles are burning down, and Grandfather is still chanting. The children are expiring with hunger, they are nodding with sleepiness, and Grandfather is still chanting! . . . Suddenly he stops, runs to the table, and quickly rattles off the grace. They begin to come to life. Uncle Itzie repeats grace after his father, at his own table. When he finishes, it's the turn of Haya Esther's orphans to say grace, one by one, and Grandmother Gittel sheds a tear. It is a long, long time before they are finally able to dip a piece of bread into the honey and to make the acquaintance of the fish and taste the pepper with the tips of their tongues!

It was even worse on the last days of the feast, and finally, one evening, on *Simchath Torah*, the Feast of the Rejoicing of the Law, Uncle Itzie could stand it no longer. He called the children and said, "Youngsters, do you want to see something interesting? Go to the synagogue, and you'll see a sight!"

He did not have to urge them, and, taking each other by the hand, they were off. It was pitch black in the street. All the other Jews were already at home having supper. Every synagogue had been closed and darkened long ago, but in the Old Synagogue there was still light.

Quietly the children opened a crack in the door and saw something they could scarcely believe. There was only one man in the whole synagogue—Grandfather. He was wrapped in his prayer shawl; he held his fat prayer book in one hand and a Scroll of the Law in the other. Tightly pressing the Scroll to his breast, he walked slowly around the pulpit and, like a cantor, recited loudly, in a sing-song, the *Hakafoth:* "Aid of the poor, save us!"

After he had gone round the pulpit once, he stopped in front of the Ark and began to dance by himself, hugging the Scroll to his breast and singing:

> Moses rejoiced in the Torah!
> Lamtedridom, haida!
> Be joyful and happy with the Torah!
> Lamtedridom, dom-dom-dom!
> Haida, dridada!
> The Torah of Moses, ha!

The children were awe-struck, and at the same time they wanted to laugh. Taking each other by the hand, they ran headlong home.

"Well, what did you see there? Wasn't it a nice spectacle?" With these words Uncle Itzie greeted them and burst out laughing until tears came to his eyes. But at that moment, the children felt a profound dislike— not for Grandfather, but for their uncle.

46　Simchath Torah

From early childhood, in the little village of Voronko,
the children had known how *Simchath Torah,* the Feast
of the Rejoicing of the Law, was celebrated. Even Uncle
Nissel, who never drank a drop too much, would douse
the whole village in wine, starting with the rabbi and
ending with the bathkeeper—even including the Russian chief of police—and would himself join in the fun
until the whole village laughed and talked about it.

After the children had left the village and returned
to their father's native city of Pereyaslov, they again
saw how this holiday infected the whole city, despite its
large Russian population. Their Uncle Pinney, that pious and God-fearing man, would start drinking wine in
the morning until, by evening, he was tipsy enough to
dance Russian dances. Those who had never seen Uncle
Pinney dance "The Cossak," earlocks and shawl fringes
flying, had never seen anything.

Uncle Pinney, when intoxicated, had another peculi-
arity which induced many thrill-seekers to follow him.
Suddenly recollecting all the quarrels he had ever had,
and who had been his enemies, he would feel compelled

to remind them of their ancient misdeeds and to curse them publicly. For example, catching David Kahanov in the street, he might grab him by his red beard and say, "Come here, you cheat, you thief, you scoundrel, you bankrupt. . . ."

Or he might spy Yankele from Krasnopolie and start off in this fashion:

"Hold on there, my little treasure! You scoundrel, pig-eater, Sabbath-breaker, you miniature of your Uncle Arnold, in-fi-del. . . ."

The interested audience surrounding them would burst into delighted laughter.

And yet the celebration of this holiday could not be compared with that seen in Boguslav, an almost completely Jewish town populated by pious Hasidim. Here the very houses, the pavements, the cobblestones, the trees, the market places seemed to dance, jump, and sing.

It was not only the adults who drank wine; the children did, too, until scarcely able to stand. Even Uncle Itzie, that dour, morose man, took a few drinks with remarkable results: he folded his earlocks behind his ears, turned up his coattails, and went off prancing a number called "The German."

But none of this could compare with Grandfather's performance. Grandfather, with no more than one small glass of brandy and half a glass of wine, became more intoxicated than a steady drinker, and behaved so madly that the city rang with his exploits.

"Did you see Moshe Yossi Hamarnik?"

"Let's see what he's doing!"

Actually, Moshe Yossi Hamarnik wasn't *doing* anything. He was merely dancing around the streets—but what dancing! He jumped, pranced, clapped his hands, and sang. Nor was he dancing alone; he danced with the Divine Spirit.

How does one dance with the Divine Spirit? Moshe Yossi held one corner of his kerchief, leaving the other free to be held by the Divine Spirit. He wheeled around and twirled, as one does with a bride; he executed all sorts of steps, forward and back, left and right, again forward and back, again left and right. . . . His head was thrown back; his eyes were shut; and a happy smile floated on his face. He snapped his fingers and sang, louder and louder each time:

> Moses rejoiced in the Torah!
> Lamtedridom, haida!
> Be joyful and happy with the Torah!
> Lamtedridom, dom-dom-dom!
> Haida, dri-da-da!
> The Torah of Moses, ha!

"Children of Israel, sing with me, sing out loud! Louder, still louder! Sing for our Torah, for our Lord! Start again, 'Moses rejoiced in the Torah! . . .'"

And the children of Israel crowded around him to watch what he was doing. All the children of the city flocked into the street to watch Moshe Yossi Hamarnik dance. They shouted, "Hurrah!" and helped him sing his joyous song in honor of the Torah. The faces of the Pereyaslov orphans burned with shame, but Grandfather was oblivious of everything. He continued the joyous dance with his beloved Spirit. He held one corner of his kerchief, and the Spirit held the other. He smiled, snapped his fingers, danced harder, and sang louder, "Moses rejoiced in the Torah! . . ." until he fainted with exhaustion. Then he was picked up and carried home. The family undressed him, removed his holiday clothes, and put him to sleep in his little room among the sheepskins.

On the following day, the world returned to normal routine and everything was forgotten. No one recalled the old man's antics of the previous day, nor did he. Nothing seemed to have changed. Swathed as always in prayer shawl and phylacteries, in his little chamber, among the sheepskins, morose and somber, he stood saying the morning prayer in a depressed voice. When it was finished, he sat down and for a long time remained bent over an ancient book.

Then, putting his book aside, he sat doing nothing at all, apparently alone with his thoughts, his somber face raised, eyes shut, far away from this world, drifting in higher spheres, divorced from the vanities of the earth, its noise and tumult.

47 *Home!*

The festive mood was supplanted by one of depression
and sorrow. Holidays gave way to daily routine when
the tabernacle was dismantled after the festival. Uncle
Itzie, that heartless man, began pitilessly to tear down
the walls. He tore off the pine-covered roof, pulled the
boards apart, and frenziedly ripped out the nails. (What
did he have against the poor nails?) But he left the
four stakes standing, and this made it worse, since they
bore witness to the carnage. They seemed to mourn and
complain, "Look, Jewish children! See what becomes of
a Jewish tabernacle?"

The men, who only the day before had been drunk
and had danced wildly and sung and frolicked like children, now became sober and respectable and almost
ashamed to meet each other's eyes. A peculiar melancholy settled over everything. Ill-temper spread through
Boguslav. But saddest and most melancholy of all were
the Pereyaslov orphans. As long as they were considered
guests, they felt comfortable in Boguslav, but as time
went on, they began to feel superfluous. Grandfather
Moshe Yossi, sitting among his sheepskins in his cubby-

hole, in prayer shawl and phylacteries, praying, studying, snapping his fingers, softly sighing and conversing with God, now paid little attention to them, except for an occasional scolding. But, long wearied of his lectures, they were more interested in the politics going on about them.

Day and night, secrets, intrigues, whispers, and gossip filled the house. Uncle Itzie and Aunt Sossie were always complaining of Grandmother Gittel—how difficult it was to drag a penny from under her pillow. They also found fault with Grandfather because he was so excessively pious and really almost senile. "He's too old," they whispered, pursing their lips into an odd smile. . . . Grandmother Gittel complained that her only son and daughter-in-law did not pay her the respect due a mother and were impatiently awaiting—oh, she knew it only too well—her death.

They had their eyes on the inheritance! But to spite them, she would go on living even though death might be a thousand times preferable to life. For what was life to her, unhappy cripple, who had buried a daughter such as Haya Esther, a mother of so many children. With her crippled hands she wiped away the tears that filled her red-rimmed eyes and called the children. She fumbled under the pillow, took out a few pennies, and gave one to each child. Little Haya Liba of the red cheeks and tiny mouth did not miss this performance, and immediately reported it to her mother, Aunt Sossie. Auntie immediately reported it to Uncle Itzie, and both of them retired to a corner to whisper about Grandmother. They were saying that for her *own* children she would stint a penny, but to the children of *others* she'd give a whole fortune. The Pereyaslov orphans heard every word, and they were not happy with their gifts. They felt miserable.

The situation in time became worse. The youngsters found themselves in the way. They saw the glances directed at them during meals. Behind their backs they heard grumblings about their ravenous appetites, and the food stuck in their throats. Long wearied with the situation, they impatiently awaited a letter from Father. When would they finally return home?

And at last, a Pereyaslov coachman, called Noah, brought the longed-for letter stating that the children were to return home. It so happened that this coachman —who was quite an ordinary coachman with the usual wagon and team of horses, and whose name was Noah, although he styled himself "Reb" Noah—had a couple of infirmities. He was hoarse, and besides, he was bald. One could, however, overlook these infirmities. As he himself explained, he became hoarse on *Simchath Torah*. That day, you see, he had a drop of brandy. That is to say, he drank brandy quite often, but this time, in honor of the holiday, he had a drop too much. As a matter of fact, they had to pump him. . . . As for his baldness, that had been caused by his obstinacy as a child. He had allowed no one to comb or wash his hair. So later, it had to be pulled out, hair by hair. . . .

All this, however, was irrelevant to the approaching journey. One thing only kept them from starting; although Noah had been sent purposely from Pereyaslov to Boguslav to fetch Nahum Rabinowitz's children, he could not withstand the temptation of looking for extra passengers. If the Lord would only send them to him, it would be an unexpected gift! For several days he haunted the market, whip in hand. His horses went on munching oats, but no passengers appeared. For the youngsters, the delay was torture.

But at last they heard the happy news: they were going! Noah had even rolled out his wagon and oiled the wheels. "Now, even though all the kings of the East and the West were to ask for a place in my wagon, it would be too late!" They could fill his wagon with gold, but it wouldn't make him stay an extra hour in Boguslav! "May this city burn to the ground! May it drown! You don't know Reb Noah! . . ."

The children rushed into the house. They prepared for the trip and said goodbye to their Boguslav friends, the Old Synagogue, the yellow Prayer House, the River Ross, their grandparents. . . . All the while Grandfather, of course, kept on lecturing and instructing them in how to be God-fearing Jews, while Grandmother Gittel kept wiping her eyes with her twisted hands. But from Uncle Itzie and Aunt Sossie they received only a cold "happy journey." They might be very pleased indeed that the "children of others" were finally leaving, but their joy was dampened by the fact that only the boys were going. The two girls were to remain in Boguslav because Grandmother Gittel would not let them go. She did not want her Haya Esther's daughters to fall into the clutches of a stepmother!

Uncle Itzie smiled maliciously, smoothed his earlocks,

and glanced at the pillow under which lay Grandmother's fortune.

"And what if the boys fall into a stepmother's clutches? Heh-heh!"

"How can you compare boys to girls? What's a stepmother to boys? A boy spends his whole day in *cheder*, but a girl stays home and nurses the stepmother's babies!"

Uncle Itzie was not satisfied. He continued to smooth his earlocks, still glancing furtively at the pillow. In order to be diplomatic, he said insinuatingly, "What would you do if all the children were girls? Heh-heh!"

"I'd keep them all with me," Grandmother replied firmly. Uncle Itzie, undaunted, continued slyly, though no longer smiling, "Where would you get the money to support so many girls?" (This time he omitted the "heh-heh.")

"God would provide it," Grandmother answered calmly. "If God helped me to raise a son like you, who can't wait till he gets my inheritance and who's afraid there won't be enough for him . . ."

"Itzie!" Aunt Sossie called from her room, "Itzie, come here! I have something to tell you! . . ."

The youngsters were delighted with Grandmother Gittel for subduing Uncle Itzie so skillfully. They were overjoyed to be finally going home. Yet one thing disturbed them—it was the word "stepmother," which they now heard for the first time. So they were to have a stepmother! What was a stepmother like? What was wrong with a stepmother that made Grandmother Gittel pity them in advance? They were terribly curious to see this stepmother of theirs.

If only they were home now!

48   Stepmother's Vocabulary

WHAT IS A STEPMOTHER?   FATHER IMPORTS A NEW HELP-
MATE.   INVECTIVE IN ALPHABETICAL ORDER.   THE FIRST
LITERARY COMPOSITION: A LEXICON OF CURSES.

Why are children told that all stepmothers are bogey-men? There was so much talk about stepmothers that the children believed a stepmother must wear horns. At every step, they heard: *stepmother!* They were warned, "You'll behave differently when you get a stepmother!" and had they not heard it said of the autumn sun, "It's no warmer than a stepmother"? There had to be something to it!

Father had suddenly disappeared. A week passed, then another, then still another. . . . Where had he gone? No one would tell the children. The grownups whispered to each other so that the children should not hear, and even then they spoke only in hints. But then, one day at *cheder,* the teacher gave the secret away by asking the children, "Hasn't Father returned from Berdichev yet?" His wife answered this diplomatically worded question by asking an even more tactful one, "Do you think it's so easy to find a stepmother for so many orphans?"

So now they knew that Father was in Berdichev looking for a stepmother. But why was this concealed from them? What made it a secret?

Just before Father returned, he wrote home that he had found someone who was eminently suitable, both from the point of view of family prestige and money, that he would soon arrive with her, and that he begged them not to let her know immediately exactly how many children he had. Why learn about it immediately? In due course she would discover it for herself. In any event, she would not have to care for all the children: the older ones were already adults, and the two girls were still with their grandmother in Boguslav. Not that he intended to wash his hands of them, God forbid! After all, children were children! But under such difficult circumstances, it would be wise to keep several of the children out of sight for a time. "There is no other news," the letter continued, "I wish you all good health, and may the Lord grant that we see each other soon and in peace."

The letter might have created a favorable impression had it not been for the remarks concerning the children. Of course, the children knew that Father loved them, that every child was extremely dear to him, but they were considerably taken aback to think that for the time being they had become contraband. This made them think odd thoughts. . . . But not for long. One day they were sent for while they were at *cheder*. "Father has returned with a stepmother from Berdichev!"

"Congratulations!" broke in the teacher's wife. "May you live to hear better news!" And the teacher dismissed the children early.

They found the entire family assembled at home. Uncle Pinney was there with his sons, and Aunt Hannah with her daughters. Everyone was seated about the table, pretending to eat cake, drink tea, and smoke cigarettes. They were chattering at random, their words making little sense, for no one was listening to anyone else; everyone was absorbed in his own thoughts. Everyone's eyes were on the stepmother, examining and appraising the "merchandise" that Father had imported from Berdichev. They seemed to be satisfied. She seemed to be very nice, tall and intelligent, and very amiable. So why all this talk about *stepmothers?* . . .

A week or two later the children understood better. It was that long before Stepmother unveiled her volatile hot temperament and her rich "Berdichev stepmother language."

The most inoffensive word she accompanied with a fitting curse uttered almost good-naturedly. For example:

Eat	—May the worms eat you!
Drink	—May leeches drink your blood!
Scream	—Scream with a toothache!
Sew	—May you be sewn in a shroud!
Go	—Go crawl on your belly!
Strike	—May you be stricken dumb!
Sit	—Sit on live coals!

Lie	—Lie under the earth!
Talk	—Talk till you're hoarse!
Hush	—Hush up for ever!
Say	—May nothing good be said about you!
Get	—Go get the smallpox!
Write	—May prescriptions be written for you!
Write off	—May you be written off as crazy!
Inscribe	—May you be inscribed in the book of death!
Prescribe	—I'll prescribe vinegar for you!

Or else she would take an innocent word like "carry" and turn it into all sorts of forms:

Carry	—May the devil carry you!
Carry in	—May you be carried in sick!
Carry out	—May you be carried out feet first!
Carry around	—May you be carried around in a coffin!
Carry away	—May you be carried away to the cemetery!

When she was in her best form she would take any word which happened to come to her lips and twist, turn, and twirl it, unwinding its undulations in a long and sinuous stream, and all in a single breath.

She also cursed in rhymes: "May the good Lord send you the ague and the plague, a rash and a brash; may you peak and pine and break your spine; may you have a fever and a pain in your liver; may you be stricken and sicken; may you be sore and roar; may you swallow pills, ache with chills, and have all sorts of ills . . . Almighty Lord!"

The hero of this biography must confess that a major part of the invective which he has incorporated in his works has been appropriated from the vocabulary of his stepmother. At an early age, before he ever thought of writing or dreamed that someday he would become an author, he was inspired, for the fun of it, to record Stepmother's invective. He gathered the material diligently and, when he had collected a considerable list, he arranged it in alphabetical order. For several nights he sweated over it, and the result was that he has a quite respectable lexicon of abuse which he can cite from memory:

A — Annoyance, ape, apostate, apple-thief, ass.

B — Bare-bottom, barker, beast, bedbug, beggar, belly-ache, belly-button, blinker, blockhead, bone-in-the-throat, boor, botcher, bottomless-gullet, brother-in-sorrow, bully, butcher.

C — Cake-and-honey, cap, carcass, cattle, cheat, cheeky, clown, cockroach, convert, cow, crazy, creature, cripple, cry-baby.

D — Dandy, devil, dirty-mouth, dog-catcher, donkey, don't-touch-me.

E — Ear-ache, eel, effigy, egg, empty-barrel.

F — Fiend, fool, foundling, frog.

G — Gambler, garbage, glutton, good-for-nothing, greedy.

H — Half-wit, Haman, hash, hen, heretic, hog, holy-seed, hoodlum, hump.

I — Idiot, image, imp, infidel, ingrate, ink-blot, innocent lamb, insect.

J — Jackal, jackass, jail-bird, Joseph-the-Righteous, junk.

K — Knock-on-wood, know-it-all.

L — Lazy-bones, leech, liar, lick-plate, locust, log, louse.

M — Melon, midget, mongrel, monkey, misery, mud, mule.

N — Nanny-goat, ninny, nobody, noodle, nuisance.

O — Onion, open-your-mouth, outcast, owl, ox.

P — Pancake, pen-and-ink, pepper, pest, pig, poison, precious, puppy.

Q — Quack, quince.

R — Rag, rat, raw-potato, riff-raff, rogue, rowdy, ruffian.

S — Sabbath-*Goy,* saint, sausage, scholar, scribbler, scum, slob, slops, smirker, snake, sneak, snout, soak, spy, squirrel, stiffnecked-people, sucker, sweet-tooth, swine.

T — Tattle-tale, thick-head, thief, thunder-and-lightning, toad, tomcat, toothache, tramp, trousers-owner, turkey, turtle.

U — Ugly, ulcer, useless.

V — Villain, vinegar, viper.

W — Wax-in-the-ears, whelp, worm, wretch.

Y — Yellow, yelper.

Z — Zany, zealot, zero.

It is possible to consider this Sholom Aleichem's first work. He entitled it "Stepmother's Vocabulary," and it was the cause of a little incident that almost ended in a dreadful catastrophe.

Since the lexicon had to be compiled in very strict alphabetical order, the author had to rewrite it a number of times. Father, apparently, noticed that the young man was working on something with unusual diligence. One evening, he came up behind him, looked over his shoulder, pulled the manuscript from him, and read it from A to Z. As if that were not enough, he read it aloud to Stepmother. But then a miracle occurred. Who knows—she may have been in a good humor at the moment, or else she was ashamed to show her anger, but the fact is that she burst into a strange laughter. She laughed so hard that everyone thought she would have a stroke. She was especially amused by "belly-button" and "trousers-owner." "Belly-button" was her name for our hero, and "trousers-owner" was her appellation for his elder brother, who had just bought a new pair of trousers. . . . Could anyone have foreseen that it would all end with laughter?

49 At the Gate

STEPMOTHER AND THE CHILDREN.   THE INN.   A LESSON
IN HOSPITALITY.   DREAMING ON A BENCH NEAR THE GATE.
A CHILD'S PRAYER.

The children learned what a stepmother can really be
like after she had presented their father with children
of her own. There were three babies in swift succession,
and no nurses or governesses to take care of them. No
nurses, that is, except their stepbrothers and stepsisters,
for that role was assigned by Stepmother to her stepchildren. It must be admitted, however, that she did not
favor her own children. She dealt out punishment liberally, pitilessly, and indiscriminately. Perhaps it was
because of this impartiality that her stepchildren felt no
malice toward the little newcomers, and treated them
with more kindness than did their mother.

Stepmother, however, did not only demand from
them such "clean" work. During that period they studied only in the morning. After *cheder,* there were chores
to do in Father's inn. There were the boots of the lodg-
ers to be polished, the samovar had to be heated, there
were errands to go on, and they had to sit at the gate
and be hospitable—that is, they had to call to the pass-
ers-by to stop and spend the night at their inn.

Do you know precisely what an inn is? It is neither a
rooming house nor a hotel, but something in between,

or perhaps a mixture of both; a place where you can get food and a night's lodging and where you can transact your business.

Nahum Rabinowitz ran such an inn in Pereyaslov, and from it he made his living. There was a large yard with stables for the horses and wagons. The bedrooms were large, and most of the rooms contained a number of beds—and each bed was rented individually. There were also private chambers for the well-to-do merchants. Very few of these came, and they were known as "fat" guests. The majority were "bed-guests," who required neither separate samovars nor service. One large samovar stood in the hall, and each "bed-guest" had his own teapot and tea. "Help yourselves, men, and drink hearty!"

Any morning or evening you would find at Nahum Rabinowitz's inn several men seated around the table drinking tea. They would all be talking at once, shouting, and smoking. The smoke would be so dense you could cut it with a knife, and the guests would be talking about everything under the sun. One of them has just come from the fair; another, a wheat merchant, is chattering about wheat, his favorite subject; a third is sick and coughs continuously—he talks about doctors; still another discusses cantors—no one can stop him, since he is obviously fond of singing; a fifth is seated in a corner, swaying as he recites the preliminary prayer in a shrill, feminine voice. . . . And the host himself, Nahum Rabinowitz, a frail man, clad in a dressing gown lined with cat's fur, with a small skullcap on his head and a fat cigarette between his lips, sits among his guests like a king among his subjects, listening to everyone at the same time. But he listens with only one ear; with the other he hears his wife's smooth-flowing invective. She is in good form. Apparently she is squaring accounts with her stepchildren. She doles out payment generously; one gets a smack in the back; another, a punch in the neck; the third, a kick in the shins. . . . One is commanded to rock the baby to sleep; another, to run to the market and help carry the baskets; and a third, to go straight to hell. . . .

The children obey. They do everything she demands, because times are bad, money is scarce. They help Father as much as they can. Some assist in the house, serving the guests; others sit outside on the bench calling to the passing coaches, "Stop here! Stop here!"

Sitting outside on the bench at the gate was naturally pleasanter than enduring the bedlam inside the house along with Stepmother's tyranny. . . . Sitting on the bench could scarcely be called work; it was almost as much fun as playing—particularly in the summer, when the coaches flew past and the coachmen yelled and whistled. They were bringing passengers from the pier, and they would race each other and raise such a cloud of dust that you would be unable to distinguish the passengers' faces. All you could see was that there was someone in the coach. . . . The children and the servants would run alongside the coach, shouting gaily, "Here, Uncle! Stop here!" The coachman's reply would be a crack of his whip; off the coach would go, leaving them standing there, feeling foolish and ashamed.

This was the way it was in summer, during the boating season, when the Dnieper was free of ice. In winter, when the river was frozen, the inn got a different type of guest. Large covered wagons came loaded with "creatures" packed in mats and reeking of smoked fish. They were not the sort of guests who hire a bed and stay over the Sabbath; they didn't object to sleeping huddled together on the floor or in the yard, next to the wagons, and they purchased nothing but hay and oats. From such guests you got little pleasure and less profit. Nor was it pleasant to sit outside on the bench in frosty weather.

The hero of this biography vividly recalls the days he spent at the gate. During the summer he would broil in the sun, and, during the winter, dressed in a tattered coat and shoes that simply pleaded to be mended, he would freeze like a dog in the cold, rubbing one foot against the other, waiting for a coach or a wagon with guests. When one came rumbling along, he would jump up to welcome it, "Here, Uncle! Stop here!" But the coaches would drive past and stop exactly opposite, at a finer inn belonging to Reuben Yasnegradsky. At Reuben's inn, it was said, the rooms were spacious and furnished with soft chairs, and they had mirrors and many other things which the Rabinowitzes did not have. For this reason, it was always jammed full of "fat" guests, whereas the Rabinowitz inn remained empty.

This was a source of great vexation to Sholom—but at whom was he angry? The answer was—God! Why hadn't God arranged for him to be born a Yasnegradsky instead of a Rabinowitz? Reuben became for him the symbol of happiness and wealth. "Fat" guests became his ideal, a new treasure about which he dreamed as he had once dreamed in the days of Shmulik. . . . Within every passing coach he imagined nothing but "fat" guests dressed in bearskins. Ah, here is one coming! Before Sholom can utter a word, the coachman stops the horses and, one by one, the wealthy passengers climb out. Yellow leather satchels are carried in, each weighing a ton and packed with all sorts of wonderful things. The guests march into the house; each one orders a private room, asks for a samovar, and calls for dinner and supper. Father comes to meet them, his face wreathed in smiles; he greets them cordially and asks whether they expect to stay for the Sabbath. The guests laugh and ask, "Why only one Sabbath, why not at least three?" The guests are merchants who have come to purchase flour; Father will get a nice commission from the deal. Then Stepmother enters. In honor of the guests, she has put a silken Sabbath kerchief over her head; her face is shining with joy; she looks at the "fat" guests, one eye closed, and asks softly, "Who brought them?" "I brought them," Sholom replies proudly, and he is happy that he has lied. There will at least be one happy day—one happy day! And what a Sabbath they will have, a happy Sabbath! But why just one? Why not three of them? . . .

All this would have been wonderful, had it not been a dream. The "fat" guests in bearskins and carrying yellow satchels did, in fact, come, and did stop—but they did not stop at their gate. They halted at the gate of Reuben Yasnegradsky. . . . "Nasty people! Why do they not come to us?" ponders the eternal dreamer, and, frozen to the bone, he enters the house. There he finds Father in his dressing gown, bending low over his books, and Stepmother in a rage. "Isn't there anyone?" What will she do with the bread she has baked and the fish she has cooked? May as well throw it to the dogs, or, "Maybe you think *you'll* get them?" she says to the children, "Poor dears, you can't possibly eat stale bread, can you? It might choke you. Your stomachs won't digest it! Such delicate creatures, the whole crowd of you, all so dainty! As if you couldn't have stayed with the girls in Boguslav! Better have you sick there than here, eating us out of house and home—may the worms eat you and gnaw you alive, may pieces of flesh fall from you as I am falling off my feet. . . ."

Here the well-known lexicon begins, and Sholom the dreamer, forgetting how cold he is, runs out into the frost again, back to the bench at the gate. It's so much better here. Here you can dream in peace about "fat" guests with fur coats and leather satchels, who may someday stop here—and not at the inn across the way. . . .

God can do anything, anything He wants!

50 *The Collector*

That frail man, quiet, thoughtful Nahum Rabinowitz,
must have had a strong character to endure Stepmother's tyranny, her endless invective, and her torturing of his children. He did not say a single word. Who
knows what his feelings were? He never revealed them,
and he hever complained to anyone. Perhaps that was
the reason his wife respected him and did not treat him
as rudely as she did his children. She was as good to him
as such a woman could be—a woman who had endured
enough suffering herself, who worked like an ox to
care for such an immensely large family, her brood as
well as his.

Perhaps her respect for her husband was also due in
part to the esteem in which she knew the city held him,
despite the fact that everyone knew he was not at all
wealthy and in fact could barely make ends meet. She
was not a stupid woman, but she had become embittered, and was unrestrained and outspoken. The moment a thought entered her head, she had to say it.
And because Father did not interfere with her, she did
not disturb him when it came to business, or book-

reading, or chess-playing, or conversation with his acquaintances.

The men with whom he liked to pass the time were young, enlightened, and well-educated. They might be called the cream of the Pereyaslov intelligentsia of those days. They deserve a more detailed description.

There was, first of all, The Collector. He was a heavy, stout fellow, very intelligent, and, as the rumor went, a bit of a freethinker, even though he still wore a long coat and earlocks. Nahum Rabinowitz considered him very deep and would say he was a man of great learning. He and The Collector would spend endless hours in discussions. Where did they find subject matter for so much conversation? Often, The Collector would bring a book with him, and often he would borrow one from Nahum Rabinowitz. His beard was always untidy, and so Stepmother had a nickname for him: Shaggy-face. But in the city he was always known as "The Collector." He was an agent for the Saxony and Braunschweig lottery tickets. Because of sore eyes he wore dark spectacles, and summer and winter he wore white socks and heavy rubber boots instead of shoes. He was very poor, but was an irrepressible optimist. He was convinced that someday one of his clients would win the first prize, in which case he would also profit. And he insisted that it would be Nahum Rabinowitz who would win it. He promised this to Nahum because, as he explained, no one needed the money as badly as he. . . . It is very possible that he said the same thing to every client—and he had many of them. Almost every Jew in the city bought a ticket in the lottery. Nevertheless, Nahum Rabinowitz had great faith in him and longed for the great prize and expected The Collector to come one day with the joyful tidings, "Congratulations, Reb Nahum, you've won twenty-five thousand!"

Our hero recalls that always, when it came to the final drawings, Father would not be able to sit still. He would sigh more than ever, yawn nervously, and shake violently as though in a fever. Sholom would be as nervous as his father, and he would look forward to the glorious day with perhaps even greater impatience. He, too, was positive that no one but his father would win. He knew every number of Father's tickets by heart. He saw them in his dreams, and he believed implicitly in God's goodness. What trouble would it be to Him to have Father's ticket win? It was so easy for the Lord, so easy. . . .

And then one day, Sholom was seated on the bench at the gate when he caught sight of The Collector striding along in his heavy rubber boots, and headed straight for their home. He jumped up and ran in to announce the news:

"He's coming!"

"Who?"

"The Collector!"

"What of it?"

"Why, today's the last day of the draw!"

Sholom saw Father's yellow face become paler. His eyes lit up for an instant—but for an instant only.

A moment later, The Collector entered, breathing heavily because of his asthma. He had to catch his breath before he could even say good morning. Father did not ask a single question. If there was anything to tell, The Collector would say it of his own accord. . . . The Collector sat down and pushed his cap back on his head. He wiped his perspiring forehead with the hem of his coat and announced the latest news:

"It's terribly hot today! It's positively roasting! Yes, it's roasting!"

There was a pause. Both men were silent. Then The Collector slowly untied a greasy red handkerchief, stained green and smelling of herring. That was where he kept the lottery tickets. With his trembling, hairy hands, he took out a large sheet of paper completely covered with figures and, through his dark spectacles, examined the paper closely, evidently searching for something. . . . Now he'd found it. He turned his dark spectacles in Father's direction.

"If I'm not mistaken, Reb Nahum, it seems your number is sixteen thousand, three hundred and eighty-four. . . ."

"I don't understand why you ask," Father replied with a smile. "I know what a wonderful memory you have. You know everyone's number by heart."

"By heart, did you say? Possibly, possibly . . . so you say it's sixteen thousand, three hundred and eighty-four? . . ."

He peered through his dark spectacles and moved his fingers over the numbers on the paper. Sholom felt his heart jump from him. *Say* it, for heaven's sake! But The Collector took his time. He spoke slowly.

"Your number, Reb Nahum, won . . . yes, it won. . . ."

Sholom saw a yellow cloud pass across Father's face for one brief moment. He had an insane desire to scream, "Cock-a-doodle-do!" but he controlled himself and drank in every word that The Collector uttered.

"You won . . . but not very much. It's a very small prize. After deducting percentages and all the expenses, you'll have no more . . . no more than . . ."

Little Sholom was expiring.

". . . no more than eight rubles and sixty kopeks. If I'm not mistaken, you owe me . . . twelve fifty, I believe. Then you have an old debt of three eighty, if you remember. If you add it all up, it amounts to sixteen thirty. And if you subtract your winnings, you'll still owe me . . . let me see . . . seven seventy . . . is that correct? Of course, you'll want another ticket! Well, you can have it. Here, Reb Nahum, choose a number! This time, by God's grace, you'll win. Believe me, that's as certain as that today is Tuesday throughout God's world! . . . Did you choose? . . . What's the number? Eight thousand, six hundred and thirteen? God grant you luck!" He turned to Sholom, "What are you staring at, you little rogue? How are you coming with *The Songs of Glory?*"

The Songs of Glory by Naphtali Hertz Weisel was a book which The Collector had brought Sholom to read, along with books by other Hebrew writers, writers such as Adam Ha-Cohen, Lebensohn, Kalman Shulman, and Isaac Baer Levinsohn. Sholom read them while sitting on the bench at the gate. Father was very proud that his son was already reading "such" books and wanted to know whether he really understood what he was reading. Sholom was too shy to say that he understood, for how could one talk about such things to Father? . . . But The Collector replied for him—*naturally* the boy understood! Why shouldn't he understand? "No doubt, it is a little too early to give such a puppy Mapu and Smolenskin to read—but these!" The Collector said; and just because he said it, the puppy was overcome with desire to read Mapu and Smolenskin. In the end he stole a couple of books by these authors from Father and read them in secret.

The first to fall into his hands was the first Hebrew novel, *The Love of Zion*, by Abraham Mapu. He read it from cover to cover in a single Sabbath, lying in the garret and burning with excitement. He shed bitter tears over unhappy Amnon, the hero of the novel, and he loved beautiful Tamar as violently as Amnon himself, and perhaps even more so. Now he dreamed of nothing but Tamar, and he talked to her in the words of the Song of Songs. He embraced her. He kissed her. . . .

The day after he had read the book he wandered about like a shadow. To Stepmother's great astonishment, he had completely lost his appetite. "What's the matter? Is the world on fire?" she asked aloud, and decided to find out why he had stopped eating.

And so it happened that *The Love of Zion* met an unhappy fate. Sholom had saved up a few kopeks from serving the guests who stopped at the inn. He spent them on a sheaf of paper which he sewed into a notebook. He ruled both sides of the pages, and started a novel in the manner of Mapu's *The Love of Zion*. A novel of his own! He followed Mapu painstakingly, imitating his language, style, and plot. Only the title was different. Instead of *The Love of Zion,* he called it *The Daughter of Zion,* and, instead of Amnon and Tamar, he called his hero and heroine Solomon and Shulamite. As he had no opportunity to write during the day—for half of his time was spent at school and the rest of the time he had to help in the inn—he wrote at night by lamplight. He wrote in tiny characters. He wrote and wrote and wrote . . . until . . . until Stepmother heard a suspicious noise and noticed light seeping through a crack in the door. She jumped out of bed, stole barefoot to the door, and discovered the young man writing blissfully. She immediately created such an uproar that the whole household awoke in fright, thinking the house was on fire. All the rumpus was because of the kerosene. "So you'll burn up our kerosene, will you? May all of you burn at the stake, merciful Lord! May all of you catch the. . . ."

Father, naturally, confiscated the unfinished novel, *The Daughter of Zion,* as well as the stolen one, *The Love of Zion,* and the young author awaited his fate. But this time he waited in vain. Father showed the masterpiece to The Collector, who could not admire the penmanship and the style enough. He pinched the boy's cheek so hard that he left a black-and-blue mark.

"Reb Nahum, you don't know what you have here! God punish me if you do! This boy is going to *be* somebody . . . wait and see! Come here, boy, let me give you another good pinch on the cheek, you rascal! . . ."

51 Superior Sons-in-Law

A MANIA FOR SONS-IN-LAW.   THE CITIZENS OF PEREYASLOV
COMPETE, AND THE JUSTICE OF THE PEACE LECTURES THEM.
LAZAR YOSSEL AND MAGIDOV, THE PEERS.   THE HERO CLIMBS
A LADDER, AND HIS HEAD SPINS.

The Collector was not the only frequent visitor to
Nahum Rabinowitz's. There were also the "superior
sons-in-law," as the younger intelligentsia, the cream of
the town, were called.

Every city has its own idiosyncracies and fashions,
and in those days sons-in-law were the vogue in
Pereyaslov. All the wealthier citizens wanted "good
catches"; it was something of a sport for them, although
a rather expensive one. Usually, the "merchandise"
was imported from a distance, for no one who could
afford better thought of making a match in his home
town. The practice was to send to Lithuania or Poland
for young men who fitted your tastes and your pocket-
book.

So Uncle Pinney imported an expert in the Torah
from Lubni. This young man belonged more to heaven
than to earth and was unable to distinguish true coin
from counterfeit. On the other hand, one of Aunt
Hannah's beautiful daughters got a man from Yagotin
who was distinguished neither for brains nor learning,
but was extremely handsome. When, on the Saturday

after the wedding, the young couple was conducted into the synagogue, they were surrounded by a crowd of oglers, disputing audibly as to which of the two was the more handsome. Since neither the "he" nor the "she" could help overhearing what was being said, they blushed to the roots of their hair, which only made them look more handsome. So long as the "merchandise" was of high quality, that is, so long as it got talked about, the parents felt amply repaid for their trouble. What else was required for popularity?

It was something to hear the respective parents quarreling about the relative merits of the various sons-in-law. The women would stick out their tongues at each other, sometimes would even fly at each other's throats, and Romanski, the shrewd Russian justice of the peace who spoke Yiddish, would have to admonish them. But he was a Gentile, and how could a Gentile possibly understand what it meant to conduct a son-in-law into the synagogue on Sabbath? No, such a one could not imagine the pleasure of leading a handsomely-dressed son-in-law to his seat at the east wall, of having him sit there on exhibition while he was treated to a reading from the Prophets, and then the final triumph of watching him ascend to the pulpit and reel off a chapter himself while everyone looked at him admiringly. No, the cleverest Gentile in the world could not fathom what it meant to a mother to have the other women rush to their little windows and ask greedily, "Where is he, where?"

Alas, too often the expensive "article" was of a type that soon wears out. For a brief moment it shone brightly, and then its luster was gone; it became just another piece of merchandise. One year, two years, and the son-in-law, yesterday's jewel, last year's prince, turned into an ordinary mortal. He grew a beard and his shoulders sagged—from worry, as anyone could see. It was then pitiful to watch him who—only last Sabbath, it seemed—had been standing at the east wall on exhibition yield the place of honor to a newer prince. How enviously the dethroned one gazed at the newcomer; and his young wife, a princess herself only yesterday, would crowd to the windows with the other women, asking, "Where is he, where?" So it is with the things of this world, and we can say with Ecclesiastes, "One generation passeth away, and another generation cometh. . . ." We might even digress into philosophy —but no, the subject remains "superior sons-in-law."

There were only two men who were exceptions to the above rule. Neither of these was superseded as quickly as the others; they were in vogue for a long time. Lazar Yossel, the first of these, was imported from Korsun to be the son-in-law of a wealthy leather merchant. In this case the bride was something less than handsome, and Lazar cost a pretty penny. Magidov, the other, came from Lithuania to be the son-in-law of a contractor whose business was supplying horses to the government. He got a pretty wife, along with board and keep, and a handsome dowry. The arrival of these two young men stood the city on its ear, and the weddings were so lavish that they were a sensation, even in the suburbs. No wonder—each had cost a king's ransom.

Whether or not the daughters were happy afterwards

is another matter. We have this much evidence to go on: one of the girls, after presenting her husband with several children, divorced him, and eventually emigrated to America. The husband of the other girl is now either a teacher or a matchmaker, possibly both. At any rate he is a poor man. However, here we are not concerned with how things turned out, but how they were. In those days the parents of the brides were in ecstasy. One of the mothers boasted that she had "bought a small curtain for the Ark of the Lord." The other spoke even more picturesquely; her purchase had been "a little Torah for the Lord's little Ark." (For the sake of the "small curtain" and the "little Torah," the Holy Ark shrank in size.)

It was all very well for them to boast; they had something of which to be proud. Lazar Yossel was a phenomenon; it was reported that he knew a thousand pages of the Talmud by heart. A thousand, mind you, not nine hundred and ninety-nine! . . . That he knew the Bible goes without saying; also that he was a master of Hebrew and rhetoric. But on the other side of the ledger were the reports (these came from homes like Uncle Pinney's) that he was perhaps a little fast, with an eye for the women. And, as for his piety, it was noted that he was not particularly fond of fasting, and had a tendency to abbreviate his prayers. Also, he carried a handkerchief in his pocket on Saturdays. Yet what insignificant weaknesses when you considered those thousand pages of the Talmud!

Magidov was also a phenomenon. He too knew a thousand pages of the Talmud by heart (not a page less!), was a master of the Bible and a wizard at Hebrew and grammar. But, unlike Lazar, he was not fast. If anything, he was a little slow and solemn. Magidov was philosophically inclined; his genius lay in contradiction. Whatever you said to him, he contradicted—a true *Litvak!*

Nahum Rabinowitz did not lose this rare opportunity to have his Bible boy tested by such extraordinary intellects. Both Magidov and Lazar tested Sholom in Hebrew, and both agreed that here was a boy whose talents must not be wasted. No doubt they praised him excessively; nor were matters improved by The Collector, who hovered close by and focused attention on himself by pointing out that he had said a long time ago that this was a boy who would amount to something. . . . The prodigy listened, drinking in every word, his heart fluttering, his soul expanding. He felt dizzy, as though he stood on a tall ladder, a shouting crowd beneath encouraging him to climb higher and higher. "There's no telling how far he'll go. . . ." Father, it was clear, was overjoyed, but then he sighed, and the sigh meant, "You never can tell about these prodigies. What I need is some practical advice. What should be done for him?"

And then finally a man appeared who could give Father the advice he wanted. This was a young philosopher called Arnold from Pidvorki. He was one of Pereyaslov's most brilliant men, and we shall devote a separate chapter to him.

52 Arnold from Pidvorki

Almost every city in the Jewish Pale had its suburbs, its
outskirts, inhabited for the most part by Gentiles and
not by Jews. The Jews who did live there were not like
those in the city. They looked more rustic, seemed bet-
ter-fed, and were somewhat coarser. They wore high
boots and smelled of sheepskins. Their laughter was
broader, with an "o": "Ho, ho, ho!" And they pronounced their "r's" hard, as if there were two of them:
"Rrabi! Rreb Morrdechai rrequests yourr prresence at
the cirrcumcision cerremony!"

Next to Pereyaslov, there was a suburb, Pidvorki,
separated from the main part of town by a brook and a
little wooden bridge. This suburb had an atmosphere
all its own. People from the city would walk there in
their free time to breathe the fresh air of gardens and
fields, and on Sabbath afternoons, young boys and girls
strolled there. Of course, the boys and girls did not
walk together—perish the thought! The boys walked
separately, and so did the girls, but once in a while,
meeting by chance on the bridge, they would stop for a
moment to exchange furtive glances or words. Some-

times they might rub elbows accidentally, and then, what furious blushes! After a number of such meetings, a secret correspondence might start up and sometimes lead to a romance. Later we shall see how such affairs could end. But, at the moment, it is Arnold from Pidvorki who interests us.

Nahum Rabinowitz had a friend called Benjamin Kalman from Pidvorki in the suburbs. A long time before, they had been partners in the wheat business, transporting wheat to Koenigsburg and Danzig by raft. But later Kalman had lost his money also. He had begun to deal in cheap staples and had to keep his nose to the grindstone. But the friendship of the former partners had remained as warm as ever. Kalman would often drop in for a chat. It was he who usually did the talking, for he loved to chatter, and he was especially fond of talking about his younger brother, Arnold. *"My* Arnold! Have you ever seen a brain like my Arnold's? A man so educated as my Arnold? As honest as my Arnold? Do you realize what kind of man my Arnold is? What other Arnold can compare with him! . . ." And so on, and on, for ever.

Everybody talked about Arnold, not only his brother, for Arnold from Pidvorki was almost a hero in the city. To begin with, he was an old bachelor—or perhaps a widower or a divorcé—at any rate, he had no wife. And a Jew without a wife is a curiosity. Furthermore, he was a notary, and whoever heard of a Jewish notary? As a matter of fact, he wasn't a notary yet, but he certainly would be one some day. Arnold had been studying to be a notary for a long time. He had only one examination to take, and then he would become a notary—unless, of course, he didn't pass. But why shouldn't he pass? "Of course, he'll pass!" said his brother. "Of course he'll become a notary! Why even talk about it—you don't know my Arnold!"

Everyone knew what a notary was. Even Sholom. There was one notary in Pereyaslov, a Russian called Novoff. But Sholom did not know what it meant to "pass an examination." What do you have to pass? To whom must you pass it? Where do you pass examinations? . . . One heard such things very often, but exactly what they meant, one did not know. For example, it was also said that Arnold wrote in the newspapers and that the whole city, Gentile and Jewish, was afraid he would write about them in *The Kievlianin*. Sholom heard what people were saying and repeated after them that everyone trembled because of Arnold's tongue and pen. It was evidently impossible to protect oneself from him, nor had anyone enough money to bribe him. "They'll get the worst of it," Benjamin Kalman said with a smile. "If my Arnold wanted to soil his hands with their affairs, he'd write them up in *The Kievlianin* from head to toe. He'd spare no one—you don't know my Arnold!"

The oddest thing about the brothers, and a very characteristic one, too, was the fact that Arnold and Benjamin Kalman, who lived under the same roof, were not on speaking terms! And yet each one boasted of the other. "My Arnold!" "My Benjamin Kalman!" No one in Pidvorki or in the city had ever seen them together or heard them exchange a single word. They would not even sit at the same table. Arnold had a room to himself in Benjamin Kalman's house. It was stacked to the ceiling with books, and there he lived, almost like a hermit. What peculiar brothers they were! And what a peculiar man Arnold was! He was one of the most frequent guests at Nahum Rabinowitz's, but his visits were not like the visits of the others. He did not come to gossip. He always brought something with him—a brand-new book, an issue of *The Kievlianin,* or just a list of grievances against the city and those who ran it.

Sholom had more respect for him than for any of the others. When Arnold came, he would not leave his side. He listened greedily to every word he said. Was this the Arnold who was to pass an examination and who would someday become a notary? Was this the Arnold who wrote in *The Kievlianin,* but who would not soil his hands? (Why did one have to soil one's hands if one wrote in *The Kievlianin?* . . .) Sholom did not take his eyes off Arnold. He liked him because he was such a pleasant, amiable man. He was not very tall; he was thin but firmly built, as if cast of steel, had a short blond beard, closely trimmed, and not a hint of an earlock. He wore a short coat, carried a slender cane, and had an extremely sharp tongue. He talked boldly about God and the Messiah, sneered at the Hasidim and disparaged fanatics, insisted that honesty was the main principle in life—and what was the use of piety? "Forget about piety—better be honest!" And his caustic laughter would ring through the room.

Sholom marveled at a Jew who dared say such things

with impunity. Apparently, Arnold from Pidvorki was allowed to say anything—only Arnold could do it!

Sometimes Uncle Pinney was present during such a conversation. He listened to Arnold's oratory, burst out laughing, and said, "Arnold! Oh, Arnold, Arnold!" This apparently signified, "How does the earth endure a godless creature like you?" But even Uncle Pinney respected Arnold for the honesty which had made him famous throughout the city. It was called "insane" honesty, for this man was obviously afraid of no one, boldly told everyone the naked truth, laughed at wealth, and had no use for money! How could one fail to respect such a man? But Arnold himself was no respecter of people. Believe it or not, he was not even impressed by Uncle Pinney! Arnold did not like Uncle Pinney, handsome though he was, and with such a venerable beard. He did, however, like Pinney's brother, Nahum, because—to quote Arnold—Nahum Rabinowitz was a man who wore no mask; he was not a mixed-up Hasid. One could talk to him about anything. One could criticize rabbis in his presence, and even Moses the Prophet! With his own ears, Sholom heard Arnold tell Father that he did not believe in the miracle of the Exodus from Egypt. "It's a legend," he said. "The whole story is simply a legend!" Sholom pondered over the word "legend" and decided that it must come from the verb "to lie"; so a legend was evidently a little lie. Thank heavens, not a big one. . . .

Once Arnold came running to Nahum with a thick volume in his hands. "Look here! See what Draper has to say about your Maimonides! Maimonides was the court physician to the Turkish sultan for thirteen years, and in order to obtain that post, he was converted! For thirteen years, your Maimonides, the author of your *Guide to the Perplexed,* was a Turk! What do you say to that?"

It was fortunate that Uncle Pinney was not present at the time.

Sholom's father must have boasted to Arnold about his son's writing, and it was from him that he sought advice. What should he do for the boy? Sholom overheard Arnold saying, "As far as his scribbling is concerned, it's worth nothing. You can throw it into the garbage! Such stuff isn't worth the paper it's written on. . . . But if you want to make him into something, enroll him in the County School. Then all sorts of paths will be open to him—the Rabbinical Seminary, if you want, or the Gymnasium!"

At this point, Sholom entered, and the men broke off their discussion. He had certainly not been pleased to hear his writings referred to as "scribbling," nor did he think the garbage can the proper repository for his work, but nevertheless Arnold had become his friend —for he had mentioned the word "Gymnasium." "Gymnasium"—the word rang in his ears like the sweetest music, although he scarcely knew what it meant; think of it—he might become a Gymnasium student! He had even seen a Gymnasium student with his own eyes. There was one Jewish boy in Pereyaslov who attended the Gymnasium. He wore silver buttons on his uniform and a silver cockade on his hat. His name was

Sholom, too, but he was called Solomon. To a chance observer, he might have seemed a very ordinary boy, but the truth was that he was very different. For wasn't he a Gymnasium student?

Arnold's advice set the Rabinowitz house buzzing. Thereafter, words like "classes," "examinations," "Seminary," "Gymnasium," and "doctor" were constantly in use. Somehow, the conversation always returned to those magical words, and everyone had something to say on the subject. All sorts of stories were told: about a poor boy from the Yeshiva who had traveled barefoot to Zhitomer to attend the Rabbinical Seminary . . . about the son of a poor Lithuanian teacher who disappeared and was thought to have taken off for America until it was discovered that he had attended the Gymnasium and was now studying medicine. . . . Only a *Litvak* was capable of such a feat! . . .

"Wait a second! The assistant surgeon—how long do you think it'll take his son to become a doctor?"

"It'll take a lot longer than one year for Yankel's son to become a doctor!"

But there is a good deal to be said about Yankel's son—and so we shall consider him in the next chapter.

53 Solomon the Student

THE "QUASI-DOCTOR" AND THE "REAL DOCTOR." THE GYM-
NASIUM STUDENT. THE DIFFERENCE BETWEEN "SHOLOM"
AND "SOLOMON." THE WINE SHOP CALLED "SOUTHERN
SHORES." KOSHER WINE FOR PASSOVER.

There were a number of doctors in Pereyaslov, and each
had a nickname of his own: "the fat doctor," "the
humpbacked doctor," "the swarthy doctor". . . . They
were all Gentiles, except for one Jew who was not even
a real doctor—Yankel, the surgeon's assistant. And yet
Yankel behaved just like the real thing; he wore a cape,
wrote prescriptions, and bellowed out the names of
medicines—in Latin, of course.

"Be so good as to take a tablespoon of *kali bromali*
every two hours, and a teaspoon of *natri bromatri* every three hours. You'll feel much better tomorrow. But
if you don't, that means your condition's worse
and you'd better send for me again. . . ."

Everyone preferred Yankel to the other doctors because he spoke their language. You could learn from
him why you had that pain in your stomach; and what
was the point of drinking fish oil for the rheumatism in
your leg (for what possible connection was there between the stomach and the leg)? He had, moreover,
one great virtue: he didn't try to overcharge you. What-

ever you gave him he accepted, without even looking to see how much it was. All he would do was feel in his pocket to see how much he'd got. If it was some measly amount, he would return it, saying that payment was unnecessary. Naturally, you'd be embarrassed, and you would give him more.

He had one other virtue: he let you do the talking, although he certainly liked to talk. He particularly liked to tell about how successful his children were. The eldest, Sholom (Solomon in Russian), was already a student in the Gymnasium. After he graduated, he would enter a university and become a doctor—a full-fledged doctor, a real doctor!

"I wish the holidays were here already," Yankel would sigh. "When my Solomon comes for his vacation, you'll have a chance to see what a student is like!"

Sholom also wanted the holidays to come quickly so that he could see what a student actually looked like.

Yankel was not very conscientious about praying, and he rarely attended synagogue. After all, why should he? He was a *doctor*. . . . But this year he did come to the synagogue on the holidays, all dressed up, his hair greased, his face glowing. He sat on the "mirror" side, opposite the east wall, and next to him sat his son Solomon, wearing a uniform sprinkled with silver buttons from top to bottom and with an odd hat on his head. The hat was adorned with a cockade. Solomon held a small prayer book in his hand, and he prayed like everyone else. You would have thought he was a human being like everyone else, just an average boy—but he was a *student!* No one could take his eyes off Solomon.

And when Yankel finished his prayers, he was in no hurry to leave the synagogue.

"Well, well, Reb Yankel, so this is the student! Shake hands!"

From all directions, hands were extended to the student. A mere boy—and bearded men were greedily shaking hands with him! Others were stopping to chat with Yankel. What was the boy studying? How long would he study? What did he intend to do when he was finished? What was he studying for?

"What for?" repeated Yankel, with a pleased laugh, "Why, you can be quite sure he's studying for *something!* He's going to be a doctor, a real doctor!"

So Yankel's son would be a doctor. . . . "Whatever happens, he'll make a living!" The older men were sure of that and they envied Yankel. Sholom, of course, couldn't understand their envy—if that was the way they felt about it, why didn't they make their children doctors? But then their fathers hadn't made them doctors, and so their children wouldn't be doctors! But they would, at least, remain good Jews. What was a living, after all? He who provides life would also provide a livelihood—the Lord would see to it. . . . For example, Uzie Finkelstein—*he* wasn't a doctor, but one should have half his money! . . .

"Well, Reb Yankel, how long, did you say . . . your student has to study?" the surgeon was asked while the boy was being scrutinized from head to foot.

"My Solomon!" Yankel replied, hopping ecstatically on one foot and smoothing his beard, "Oh, he still has a long way to go!" And on his fingers he began calculating how many more years Solomon had to spend in the Gymnasium, and then in the university, and then as an intern in a hospital or on service in a military hospital. . . . If he entered a military hospital, he could become a doctor in the army, and that was almost like being an officer . . . with epaulets!

And where could you have found a happier creature than Yankel, our assistant surgeon, standing there with his pushed-in nose and kinky hair and wearing a cape just like a real doctor. Nor was there a more fortunate creature than his son, that apple-cheeked student with his silver buttons and the odd hat. The two left the synagogue surrounded by a crowd of men and boys. The men crowded around Yankel, and the boys around the student; the boys got as close as possible. This boy was a creature from a different world—he even smelled different!

Never did Sholom envy anyone so much as that student. Why wasn't *he* in his shoes? Why wasn't *he* Yankel's son? Wasn't his name Sholom, too? . . .

Subsequently, Sholom dreamt about Yankel's Solomon night and day; he did not stop thinking about him. He became a sort of mania with him, an *idée fixe,* another Chaim Fruchstein. . . . He envied him, but he lacked the courage to come closer and speak to him. How did one talk to a student? How could one approach a boy whose name was Sholom but who was called Solomon? . . . But in his imagination he saw himself as a student. Now he wasn't called Sholom any longer; he too was Solomon, and he also wore a uniform with silver buttons and had a cockade on his hat. All the boys and men would crowd about, marvelling. "Is this the student son of Nahum Rabinowitz? Is this the boy we used to call Sholom? . . ."

With what joy Sholom heard his father announce one day that he and his brother would begin attending classes the following day! Father had already seen the principal and had filed an application for Sholom to enter preparatory school.

"After you finish the preparatory school—that's six weeks—you'll enter the County School, and afterwards, God willing, maybe even a school of higher education. . . . Everything is within God's reach. Only you have to try very hard!"

If Sholom had not been in his father's presence, he would have shouted with joy. Would he try hard? What a question! He scarcely knew the meaning of half that was being said—"County School," "principal," "preparatory school"—but he remembered Arnold's words and Yankel's son decked out in uniform. . . . His head spun and tears of joy filled his eyes. But he remained standing before Father, like an innocent who doesn't know how to add two and two. He was waiting for the moment when he would be alone. Then he would let himself go! He'd throw himself on the ground and turn triple somersaults. He'd hop about on one foot, singing lustily:

> Solomon, Solomon—
> Student, student Solomon!

"Sholom, please go rock the baby, and then you might help me chop the raisins. . . ."

This, of course, came from Stepmother. Should the reader wonder why raisins must be chopped, he must be informed that since he had been unable to make a living from his inn, Nahum Rabinowitz had opened a wine shop. Above the shop he hung this sign:

OUR WINES COME FROM SOUTHERN SHORES

These southern wines Nahum made from chopped raisins. The wine was always made from raisins, but it was given various names: there was "Cherry Wine," "Madeira," "Sherry," and one wine called "Kosher Wine for Passover," which was a favorite of the children because it was sweet and strong. This sweetness was caused by a syrup which was added to the wine, and its strength lay in the raisin-pits. But how it got its red color was Father's secret. . . . Every time the children were sent to the cellar for a quart of wine, they helped themselves to a few swigs of kosher wine for Passover. Yet, oddly enough, this business prospered—at any rate, better than anything previously undertaken by Nahum Rabinowitz.

54   The Prize

Events are quicker in the telling than in the doing. The
process of entering the County School was a long and
difficult one. To begin with, there was Unce Pinney,
who was half beside himself. "How can one send one's
own children to be made into Gentiles?" Nor was he
mollified until his brother gave him his word that he
would not permit the children to write on the Sabbath.
And so Nahum Rabinowitz and the principal agreed
that the boys would not attend school on the Sabbath.
Nahum elicited another concession (for in those days
Jews were able to win concessions): the boys would not
attend class during the lessons on religion.

There was a second difficulty—language. Sholom and
his brother spoke Russian so poorly that the teachers
and students ridiculed them; it seemed to the boys that
the very benches laughed. For Sholom this was particularly mortifying; he who had once laughed at others
was now being laughed at himself. Nor were the Gentile boys caught off their guard. No sooner had the Jewish children entered the schoolyard their first day than
their Christian classmates overwhelmed them and good-
naturedly smeared lard on their lips. That evening Na-

hum Rabinowitz's sons returned home fearful that, should they tell what had happened, they would not be permitted to return to school.

And then there was Stepmother, who positively hounded the "scholars"—her new name for the boys. Sholom was the more diligent of the two, and this made her torment him. But one day she overstepped the mark, and that put an end to her domination.

That morning Sholom was, as usual, pacing up and down the room, memorizing his lesson; Father was praying, and Stepmother was occupied with nagging Father and reminding him of his ancient transgression: the fact that a few of the smaller children had slipped his mind when he had originally told her about his family. This subject having been exhausted, she dealt next with the subject of his children's enormous appetites. Nor did she forget to bring in his more remote relatives. A fine crowd they were! But none of this seemed to perturb Father. He stood facing the wall and continuing to pray as if none of this really concerned him. And then, finally, it was Sholom who got it for marching around the room while studying.

"Here's a fine scholar who thinks he's second cousin to the Sultan. Now that he's royalty, he imagines he doesn't have anything else to do but eat. From the way he acts you'd suppose we had a whole houseful of servants. Now, my fine down-at-the-heels scholar, don't you think you could make a slight effort? It wouldn't break your back to carry the samovar up to our guests, and it certainly wouldn't hurt your appetite."

Sholom would have dropped everything and fetched

the samovar from the kitchen, had not Father rushed to him and grasped his hands. Father was very excited, but, even so, he remembered to speak in Hebrew so as not to interrupt the prayer.

"No, no! It's out of the question . . . I won't permit it!" In his excitement, he began to speak in Yiddish, and, perhaps for the first time since their marriage, he shouted at Stepmother in anger. She must never order Sholom about again. With the other children she could do as she wished. But Sholom was not like the others—Sholom must study.

"Once and for all, I want it understood. That's how it'll be."

Perhaps it was because every despot fears a voice louder than his own, or possibly because this was Father's first show of opposition—whatever the reason, a miracle came to pass. From that day on, Stepmother kept her peace; she became quite another person in her dealings with Sholom. Not that her invective ceased; she still continued to complain about the tons of paper he consumed and the three bottles of ink he used daily. She still "forgot" to fill the kerosene lamp at night and to prepare breakfast for him in the morning. But now she never required his help about the house. Of course she did not object to his running an errand if he wished, or rocking the baby, if the mood came over him. But it had to be of his own free will.

"Sholom," Stepmother would inquire in her soft Berdichev singsong, "Isn't it odd that as soon as you look at the samovar, it begins to boil?" Or, "Have you noticed that the baby falls asleep as soon as he's in your arms?" "Sholom, it wouldn't take you very long to skip to the market. I'll bet you could be back in half a minute. . . ."

It never rains but it pours. One day in class, the superintendent, a very charming man, took Sholom by the ear and told him he wanted to see his father. When Nahum Rabinowitz learned of the superintendent's invitation, he did not have to be coaxed. He put on his Sabbath coat, curled his already well-curled earlocks further behind his ears, and went off to hear what it was about. His son Sholom, he learned, was doing so exceptionally at the school that he was entitled by law to a scholarship consisting of full maintenance by the Government. However, since he was a Jew, all he would get was a cash prize amounting to about one hundred and twenty rubles a year.

This event created a furor in the city. People came from everywhere to learn if it was true.

"What should it be? Did it seem like a lie?"

"A real scholarship?"

"Yes, a real one."

"And from the Government?"

"No, from the Ministry of Public Education."

It was no small matter to be in touch with a ministry!

That evening, the entire family assembled to gaze at the scholarship boy, and even Stepmother was in a good humor. The guests got tea and preserves as a consequence, and she almost looked beautiful to Sholom.

The past had vanished; he forgave her her sins. He was the hero today, and everyone was staring at him. They were all talking about him, laughing, and rejoicing. Aunt Hannah's children, always fond of teasing him, asked him what he intended to do with so much money. As if they didn't know! It would all go to Father and his Southern Shores Wine Shop.

And then, there he was at last, the stout Collector—as always, wearing his dark spectacles and rubber boots. He came to have a good look at the young rascal, to pinch his cheeks. Nor did Lazar Yossel and Magidov, the superior sons-in-law, forget to congratulate Father, although they also came, it seemed, to discuss enlighenment, progress, and civilization. But when Arnold from Pidvorki came somewhat later, he put a damper on everyone's joy. Obviously, they didn't know what they were talking about. This wasn't a scholarship at all; it was a cash prize. A scholarship was one thing, a cash prize another. . . . Nor had Sholom been the only boy to get one. Another student in the County School had also been given one hundred and twenty rubles. This was Sholom's friend Elie. But the words of Arnold from Pidvorki could not spoil Sholom's happiness. Once more he dreamed of Shmulik and the treasure. . . . Once more his imagination carried him away into a land of fancy. His father inhabited this country too, but he had changed. He had become young again. What had happened to the lines on his forehead, to his stooped shoulders, to his pale, careworn face? These had gone, and with them, his habit of sighing. . . . Sholom stood with Father in the midst of the family. Think of it, he was famous! His name was known to the Government, to the Ministry of Public Education . . . perhaps even to the Czar himself! . . . Anything was possible!

55 *Sholom's Friend Elie*

ELIE DODI'S.   FIRST ENCOUNTER DURING A FIRE.   SCIEN-
TIFIC DISCUSSIONS WITH UNCLE PINNEY.   OUR HERO OPENLY
VIOLATES THE SABBATH.   CRIME AND PUNISHMENT.

A white, round face, slightly pockmarked; stiff, prickly, coarse, thick, black hair which stood on end; laughing eyes; strong, white teeth; stubby fingers; a ringing explosive laugh; a hot temper—these make up the portrait of Elie—Elie, who was Sholom's friend all through school.

They became acquainted the night of the fire.

A fire in a small town is a spectacle; it is a free show, which affords a highly interesting aggregation of all kinds of characters in all sorts of situations, both comic and sad. The night is still, and the stars twinkle. Somewhere a dog is howling. The small house burns peacefully and slowly, like a candle.

People stream out onto the streets. They come sleepily, but they grow more excited and more boisterous. They come singly at first, then in groups, and, finally, a crowd of Jewish children arrives. Men wearing *arba kanfoth* rush into the fire; women shriek; little children cry; young boys wisecrack, and girls titter. The Rabinowitz children are there too. Suddenly Sholom hears a boy's voice next to his ear:

"They're coming!"

"Who?"

"The firemen. Let's help them put out the fire!"

The two boys run hand-in-hand across the market place toward the firemen. Sholom learns that his friend is called Elie and that he is the son of Dodi, the scribe.

Their second meeting took place later, by day. A swarthy man with a trained monkey had every boy in the city running after him. It was one of those street shows which were occasionally seen in Pereyaslov. Now and again there would be a blind bear that danced with a stick; or a Punch and Judy show with Punch in red trousers; or else there would be the gypsy with his monkey. The gypsy and the monkey looked very similar; one could almost believe they had been born of the same mother. Both had wrinkled, hairy faces, bald heads, and pitiful eyes. They stretched out thin, hairy, dirty hands and begged. The gypsy had an odd voice and spoke in a strange language. He made such funny faces that one couldn't help laughing. "Give, mister! Good monk! Americano!"

From these two meetings came the friendship between Elie Dodi's and Sholom Rabinowitz. Their first day at school found them in the same class, sitting on adjoining benches. Sholom's new friend stretched out his hand, shook his head, and mimicked the gypsy's expressions. "Give, mister! Good monk! Americano!" How could they keep from laughing? Their friendship was sealed forever when they were both punished by being deprived of lunch.

From then on, they were inseparable. Wherever one went, the other followed. They studied together and promised each other to excel their Gentile schoolmates. But, although they were always at the top of their class, they took liberties no other boy would dare—for weren't they honor students, prize winners? How well they knew Russian grammar! They could immediately conjugate any verb mentioned. So, if you said, "What's this I hear about you kids?" they'd answer at once, "Hear about you, heard about him, hearing about her, have heard about them!" And they knew science as well as grammar. The paths of heaven and earth were as familiar to them as the streets of Pereyaslov. Why the earth is round; whether the earth revolves around the sun, or vice versa; where wind comes from; and which comes first, thunder or lightning—these things were all known to them.

Of all the subjects taught in school, Nahum's father thought most highly of natural science. Science was a subject which broadened and instructed the mind. Mathematics was valuable also, because it sharpened the brain, but it had no further use. Take Yossi Fruchstein—he was quite an ordinary man who had never studied anywhere, and yet if you gave him the most difficult mathematical problem, he'd solve it in his head! Or take The Collector. Where had he studied? In some *Litvak* Yeshiva! And yet he could manage algebra! There was no need to bring in Lazar Yossel or Arnold from Pidvorki. Why, Arnold was ready to take any examination! No, say what you like, science was different from mathematics. Science required study. Science was something one had to *know!* . . . And Sholom knew science, and Father liked to discuss it with him, particularly when someone else was present.

It was best of all when the someone was Uncle Pinney. Uncle Pinney would run his hand through his beard and smile knowingly at the young scientist. Unbelievable as it may seem, he had just been informed that the earth revolved about the sun, and not the other way around! "Well, how do you explain what it says in the Scriptures: 'Sun, stand thou still upon Gibeon'? That you can't answer, eh? Next thing you'll be claiming thunder comes before lightning," Uncle Pinney would say, shaking with laughter. "And no doubt you think the earth is a ball, round as an apple. Can you prove it?"

Sholom would reply, "Try getting up early tomorrow and, when the sun rises, look at the top cupola of the monastery. You'll see that it will light up before anything else. . . ."

"That's fine! I've got nothing better to do than get up at sunrise and look at the monastery!"

Uncle Pinney did not think well of science, nor, for that matter, of the school, nor of the friendship between Sholom and Elie. Elie Dodi's would lead Sholom heaven alone knew where. . . . Uncle Pinney had heard things about them. For instance, he'd heard that one Sabbath they'd taken a walk in Pidvorki carrying handkerchiefs and talking Russian. . . .

Unfortunately, it was all too true! What's more, they went to Pidvorki every Sabbath, and not merely for the sake of taking a walk (as we shall see later). Moreover, they carried with them not only handkerchiefs, but even money to buy pears, and they spoke about *such things* in Russian. . . . Oh, if only Uncle Pinney had known what they spoke about! . . . If Uncle Pinney had known that the two young gentlemen went rowing and sailed far down the river, or lay on the green grass, read Russian books, sang Russian songs, and dreamed aloud about the future. . . . They spoke of where they would go after leaving the County School, what they would study, what they would become. . . . To be honest, there was nothing really Jewish in those dreams. Elie had been raised in a home in which Judaism had played only a small part, although (since one thing, apparently, had nothing to do with the other) he had been slapped as much for skipping prayers as any other child. I am afraid all fathers are alike. Even today you find parents who do not practice what they preach. . . .

From their earliest days, the children had had a chronic aversion to prayers, and, after they entered school, they stopped praying altogether. Although Father knew that this was so, he pretended not to notice. But there were plenty of others who kept their eyes wide open and undertook to open Father's as well. His children were forsaking the path of righteousness.

Such nagging, however, merely increased the youngsters' repugnance, and they experienced an almost spiritual pleasure in their rebellion. Not in vain had they been taught the meaning of sin. Sin, they had learned, was not dreadful in itself; it was the pleasure experienced in committing sins that was evil. To this day, Sholom can still savor the taste of his first great sin.

Sabbath noon. It is after dinner, and people are taking their afternoon naps. There is not a soul in the streets. There is absolute silence. The sun is as hot as in the desert, and the painted walls of the house and the wooden fences in the yard simply beg to have something written on them. Sholom's hands are in his pockets, and he fingers a piece of chalk. He looks around—not even a shadow in sight. The shutters are tightly closed. The Tempter urges him, "Go on, draw something!" But what should he draw? He quickly sketches a picture of a man and sings the Russian ditty, well-known to little children, which always accompanies it:

One dot, two dots, and a comma;
  Minus sign—the face a keg!
One arm, two arms, and a circle;
  Belly-button, leg and leg!

The little mannikin with the round face, two hands, two legs, and a laughing mouth is finished. The artist is tremendously pleased with the portrait. Only an inscription is lacking. He looks about him again—still no one in sight, and all the shutters are still closed. The Tempter whispers, "Write!" What shall he write? He takes the chalk, and under the picture he writes the familiar Russian rhyme, in handsome round characters:

> Whoever wrote this, I don't know.
> You are a fool to read it, though!

And before he can re-read what he has written, he feels a pair of fingers pinching his left ear.

I am sure none of my readers can guess who caught our hero at the dreadful sin of violating the holy Sabbath. It was none other than Uncle Pinney! Just this day, Uncle Pinney *had* to wake before anyone else and be the first to come to Nahum's with Sabbath greetings! . . . It is unnecessary to describe what followed. Neither pleas nor tears were of any use. Uncle Pinney grabbed Sholom, smeared with chalk as he was, and led him straight home to his father. But this was only a trifle compared to what happened when the city learned of the affair. The authorities of the County School very nearly expelled the boy. Father wept and pleaded with the principal. And he was pardoned only because he was an honor student and had won a prize. But the teachers gave him a new new nickname. Now, when they called him to the blackboard, they no longer addressed him as "Rabinowitz." Now it was always "Artist" or "Author," and they stretched out the word until it was almost two yards long: "Au—thor!"

And that name remained with him for a long time—indeed, forever!

56   *Among Cantors and Musicians*

For as long as he can remember, the author of these
memoirs wanted to write. He wanted to write with more
than chalk on walls. And his old friend, The Collector,
prophesied that he would. Someday he would be a
writer like Zederbaum, Gotlober, or Yehalel. But Arnold from Pidvorki had other plans for him; he would
be a writer, yes; but he would write in Russian, not in
Hebrew. He said, "There are enough dilettantes and
ignoramuses in the 'Hamelitz' journal. Let him take as
his ideal not Zederbaum or Gotlober—but Tur-
genev, Gogol, Pushkin, or Lermontoff!"

In other words, the alternatives were Hebrew or Russian! But it never occurred to anyone that Sholom
would someday write in Yiddish. After all, could you
consider Yiddish a language? Everyone, naturally,
spoke Yiddish, but who thought of *writing* it! Yiddish
was referred to as *"Ivre-Taitch,"* that is, a jargon good
only for women. A man would be ashamed to be found
with a Yiddish book in his hands; one did not want to
be taken for an ignoramus!

Yet a significant event occurred in Sholom's childhood. A book written in the despised "jargon" had a
great success in the God-forsaken village of Voronko. It

is difficult now to recall what the book looked like other than that it was small and thin and that its pages were yellow and tattered. Nor did the book have either a cover or even a title-page.

It was one Saturday evening and all the property-owners had gathered at Reb Nahum Vevik's to usher out Queen Sabbath. Mother was busy in the kitchen preparing a "Wallachian *borscht*," and, while everyone was waiting for it, Reb Nahum amused his guests by reading from the book. His guests sat around the table, smoking cigarettes and roaring with laughter as he read aloud to them. Every other minute they interrupted the reader to express their delight. "The cunning devil! Now that's something, isn't it!"

Even the reader was unable to keep from laughing. None of the children wanted to go to bed—nor did Sholom. He understood little of what was being read, but he enjoyed watching the bearded Jews roar and chuckle. He looked at the delighted faces about him and envied the man who had written that book. When he grew up he wanted to write books that Jews would read and which would make them laugh. . . .

One thing was certain: whether or not he would someday write, and whether it would be in Hebrew or Russian, he would not be an ignoramus! He wanted to know everything; he wanted to learn everything—even such things as playing the violin. One may ask, "But what has a violin to do with education?" Well, there was a connection; in those days, violin playing was part of the course of study. So, also, children of good families studied German and French, although no one expected any practical use to come of it. It was just that such children had to know *everything*. The sons of the finest families studied the violin. Chaim Fruchstein, for instance, and Tzali Merpert and Mottel Sribny. Many of the younger boys took violin lessons as well. Was Sholom Rabinowitz less endowed than they? . . . But Father would not hear of it. "It is useless," he said, "a complete waste of time. Mathematics, geography, rhetoric—those make sense. But what kind of work is scratching on a fiddle?"

Yet Joshua Hershel had another view. No one could deny that, despite being a musician, he was a God-fearing man. Did he not wear thick, heavy earlocks and was he not learned? "What has one got to do with the other?" he asked. He had children of his own, and they were no worse than other Jewish children and quite able to take care of themselves—no one pushed them around! But they played every instrument imaginable. . . . Bentzion, the violin teacher who taught all the boys to play, also had something to say. He had given Sholom two lessons from the first book of Beriot. In the presence of all the children, he announced in his characteristic snuffle (his nose had been slightly broken) that the boy had "falenf," which, in his idiom, meant "talent." Sholom didn't know whether this was true or not. But he did know that he had always wanted to play the violin. And, as if fate wished to tantalize him, he was forever finding himself in the world of music, among cantors and instrumentalists.

There was never a lack of cantors and choir boys in

his home because Nahum Rabinowitz enjoyed praying before the altar and was a connoisseur of fine singing. Moreover, his inn was the place where cantors stopped when they came to town. Not a month passed that some wagon did not drive up crammed full of odd-looking people who looked almost like beggars, so ragged were their clothes. This would be a cantor arriving with his choir boys. But although the choir boys were ill-clad, practically naked, in one respect they were more than adequately dressed—their throats were always wrapped in warm woolen scarves. When it came to food they were locusts and devoured everything in sight. Hunger was the trademark of the choir boy.

Throughout the day, the master, the "world-famous" cantor, would practice his coloratura. He would eat an infinite number of eggs while his choir boys toiled. For the most part, their voices were weak and thin; but they had tremendous appetites. Their method of prayer did not particularly appeal to the congregation, and they ate and drank, and left without paying their bills. Naturally, this did not endear them to Stepmother, and one by one she removed the "world-famous" cantors from the inn. They should be good enough to stop at Reuben Yasnegradski's, across the way, because here there were more than enough "eaters" and "shouters."

So it happened that the children of Nahum Rabinowitz came to know the composer of every sacred litany —whether it was Cantor Pitzie, Cantor Mitzie, the Kashtaner Cantor, the Siedlitzer, the Kalvarier, or Nissie Beltzer. . . . There were times when song seemed to have frozen in the air; tunes swirled in one's head and kept one from falling asleep.

Sholom had an especially good opportunity to hear music since both Joshua Heshel and Bentzion lived near the school. He passed their homes on his way to school. Nothing really forced him to pass their homes; in fact, another way would have been shorter. . . . Sholom, however, loved to stop beneath their windows and listen to Bentzion teach the violin, or Joshua Heshel conduct an orchestra composed entirely of his own children. No one could have chased Sholom away from those windows. Sometimes one of Joshua Heshel's children would see him there. Once, the eldest, called Hemeleh, used his bow on him; another time, he doused him with water. But in the end, thanks to a cigarette, he soon made friends with Hemeleh and became a constant visitor at Joshua Heshel's. He never missed a Monday or Thursday rehearsal and, in this way, soon became acquainted with the whole circle of musicians. He knew their families, the idiosyncrasies and habits of their Bohemian life, and even their musical jargon, some of which he later used in his works "On the Violin," "Stempenu," "Wandering Stars," and others.

Clearly, he was predestined to learn to play the violin. He had heard enough music, and Bentzion had called him talented. What else was needed? All he required was a violin—but violins were expensive, and he had no money. What was to be done? Obviously, get money. . . .

And, because of this, a strange thing happened which was both comical and sad—a sort of tragi-comedy.

57 Thou Shalt Not Steal

THE LODGER'S PURSES. THEFT AND REPENTENCE. HOW
TO GET RID OF ILL-GOTTEN GAINS.

Among those who stopped at Rabinowitz's inn there was
a perennial guest, a Lithuanian wheat merchant from
Pinsk whose name was Wolfson. He would stop at the
inn for months at a time. He was always given the same
room, which, even in his absence, was called "Wolfson's room," and he had a samovar of his own. The Rabinowitzes regarded him as one of the family—he ate
what they ate, drank what they drank, and when Stepmother was in a bad humor he got his share along with
the others. In the house he wore a smoking jacket. Sometimes he even walked around the house without it, smoking enormous cigars. Clenching his cigar between his
teeth, hands deep in his trouser pockets, he would chatter endlessly. The door of his room was always ajar, his
samovar always on the table; the table drawer was shut,
but the keys hung in the lock. . . . All one had to do
was turn the key and the drawer would open. Everyone
knew what was kept in the table drawer. There were
books and ledgers, letters, accounts, and money. . . .
One large, plump wallet, stuffed with paper bills, must
have contained a fortune. There was also a leather purse,
old and peeling, but always full of silver and copper

coins which surely must have added up. . . . If a boy like Sholom had only half of it, he would have had enough to purchase the finest violin in the world. . . .

Wolfson would often open the drawer in plain sight, and Sholom could not help seeing the wallet, stuffed with bills, and the leather change purse. He was particularly attracted by the latter and his most cherished dream was that someday Wolfson would lose his purse and that he, Sholom, would find it.

"Returning lost property" is certainly a noble act, but to own a change purse is even nobler. . . . But the Lithuanian simply refused to lose it! Sholom was willing to settle. If Wolfson were to let him dust his trousers, leaving the purse in the pocket, could anyone blame Sholom if, during the dusting, the purse were to slip out accidentally? . . . But Wolfson was no fool. He always emptied his pockets before giving the children his clothes to dust. What can you do with a *Litvak?* Irritated, Sholom decided that if Wolfson wouldn't lose his purse or misplace it, Sholom could at least take a peek inside, just to count the change. . . .

So it was out of mere curiosity that one morning Sholom entered Wolfson's room. He loitered a bit, pretending to straighten up the table, while the Lithuanian was in the hall, the fat cigar in his mouth, gabbing away as usual. No matter how carefully Sholom fingered the cold keys, they seemed to him to give off a tremendous clatter. His legs and arms trembling, he turned and left Wolfson's room.

The first attempt was a failure, and he had to wait for another opportunity. Meanwhile, he admonished himself, "You are a thief, Sholom! The mere thought makes you a thief, a thief, a *thief*. . . ."

He did not have to wait long for another opportunity. Wolfson did not like to sit alone in his room. When there were other guests in the main room, he liked to spend his time with them, smoking and chatting. And so, one day, Sholom again slipped into Wolfson's room. He leaned over the table, pretending to get something on the other side, and his left hand grasped the keys. A turn to the right . . . and the lock opened with a soft ring—then, quiet. Trembling, he looked into the drawer and saw the thick wallet packed with paper money: red ten-ruble bills, blue five-ruble bills, green three-ruble bills, yellow one-ruble bills. . . .

Heaven knows how much money there was! If he were to pull out a single red bill, who would miss it? Go ahead, fool, take it! But no, he couldn't. His hands trembled, his teeth chattered, and breath fled from him. He glanced at the leather purse—it was bulging. He wanted to seize it, but his right hand refused to obey. Might it not be a good idea to open the purse and take a few silver coins—but that was too much work. If he took the purse and put it in his pocket, it would soon be discovered. . . . Each minute felt like a year. Then he heard a noise—the Lithuanian shuffling about in his slippers. . . . Sholom quickly turned the key and again left the room empty-handed. He expected to run into someone, but there wasn't a soul in the corridor. Should he return? It was too late. Such an opportunity lost! "You're an idiot, Sholom, you're both a thief and an idiot!"

The third attempt was successful. Disregarding pre-
liminaries, losing no time, he went straight to the table, turned the lock, thrust his hand into the drawer,
pulled out the purse, put it into his pocket, shut the
drawer, and was off to school with his books. He did not
hurry. He was calm, almost indifferent. But after he
had left the house, the purse seemed to burn his flesh
through his pocket. He couldn't possibly keep it there
—certainly not during the first day. So instead of going
straight to school, he detoured to the woodshed and
hid the purse in a dark corner, between the lumber and
the wall. He carefully noted the spot so as to remember
it, and hurried off to school.

Have you ever met anyone with a wild distracted expression, who seemed at the point of sacrificing himself for some great unknown cause? Such a person has a
secret known only to himself and to God. This was
how Sholom looked on that memorable morning. Sinner that he was, he looked everyone straight in the eyes,
yet it seemed to him that everyone knew he was har-
boring a dreadful secret. "What's wrong, Sholom," his
friend Elie asked him, "have you been drawing pictures
on the fence again?" "Shut up, Elie, or I'll draw out
your liver!" "Is that so! All right, try it!" and Elie
rolled up his sleeves, preparing for battle. But Sholom
was in no mood for a fight. All he could think of was
the purse in the woodshed.

In his haste he had even forgotten to count the money
in the purse, and he could barely live until class was
dismissed, when he could hurry home to the shed to

take a hasty look at the contents of the purse. How much money would he find?

He arrived home to find the house in a turmoil. The bedding had been ripped off the beds. The kitchen was topsy-turvy. The servant girl was protesting that she knew nothing about it. Father was stooping more than ever and his face was black with anger. Stepmother was raging and cursing. No one knew quite who she was cursing. "May the devil steal them as they stole it! . . . May the earth swallow them up as it swallowed the purse! . . . No one has seen the purse, may they never see again! . . . Who'll stop at our inn now? May they stop breathing. . . ." Wolfson was there also, dressed in his dressing gown, fat cigar between his lips, hands in his pockets. He looked at the children, smiled, and talked to himself. "I know I had it this morning . . . and I haven't left the house for a minute. . . ."

"Have you seen the purse?" Father asked the children, and Sholom answered for everyone.

"What purse?"

Father seldom lost his temper, but this time he couldn't control himself.

"What purse! All morning long, you hear nothing but purse-purse, purse-purse, and now you ask 'what purse'!" And then he turned to Wolfson.

"How much money was in it?"

"It isn't a question of money; it's a question of principle!"

This was clearly not the time to examine the purse. Sholom realized he must wait for a more auspicious moment. In the meantime, he had to get down to his books. He had some geography and history and a few theorems in geometry to learn, and he sat studying them while, all about him, the house was in ferment. The servant was dismissed by Stepmother in a rage and the search for the purse continued. Finally, Sholom joined the searchers. Only now did the thief realize what an evil thing he had done. Now he was sorry; now he was penitent; he could not bear to look at Father's worried face. . . .

Each hour seemed like a year, and the day an eternity. But Sholom managed to survive until evening. The excitement had somewhat abated. This was his opportunity, and the little thief slipped into the yard. He hurried to the shed and pulled out the purse and looked into it. . . . In it was an ancient, worn coin which had once been worth ten kopeks. Now it was probably not even worth one. . . . And such an ugly purse with such a useless lock. The leather was old and greasy, the corners wrinkled and yellow, like the skin on an old woman's face. . . . It was a repulsive purse—and for this disgusting thing he had sinned, he had violated the commandment: Thou shalt not steal!

When he returned to the house, Stepmother gave him the honor of carrying the samovar to Wolfson's room. Whenever the samovar was served, it was Wolfson's habit to rub his hands and sing out in rhyme, "Hi-diddle-dee, we'll have some tea! That pleases me!" This time he added a question. "Well, what's the news? Have they found it?" He looked into the boy's eyes intently, and there was irony both in his words and gaze. Or perhaps Sholom only imagined it. (What is the saying? —the cat knows whose cream she has eaten; the stolen cap burns the thief's head.)

From that moment, Sholom the Thief hated Wolfson with all his heart and soul. He hated his *Litvak* face and his *Litvak* accent. He cursed him and his purse also. And what was he to do with the repulsive thing he had stolen? He could not leave it in the shed to be discovered. Suspicion was sure to fall on the children. This time he'd really done it.

It took him a long time to get to sleep that night. He could scarcely believe that it was not all a dream. Had it really happened? Was he actually a thief? He began to sweat. How could he have fallen so low! . . . What crime would he commit next?

When he finally fell asleep, he dreamed about purses, but they were not real purses; they were alive and squirming horrors; they were wrinkled and yellow, and cold and wet like toads. . . . They moved and crawled all over his body. They climbed under his collar and beneath his armpits. . . . He woke suddenly, looked under the blanket, and felt his body all over. . . . Thank heavens, it was only a dream! . . . But how was he to get rid of the purse?

The only solution was to leave it where it would not be found. But where? Perhaps the garden of their Gentile neighbors? Or the cemetery? Or what about the women's section of the synagogue? No! The best thing would be to throw it from the bridge, into the river. And the best time would be on Sabbath.

And that is what he decided to do.

287

Sabbath afternoon, the end of the summer. Outside, it was still warm. Children were running about lightly clad, the girls still carrying parasols. Sholom moved with the other strollers, the purse buried in his pocket —but now filled with stones, so that it would go straight to the bottom of the river. But his act must not be seen, and the bridge was crowded. He wandered through the crowd, peering into the faces about him, and every eye seemed to accuse him. . . . It was the old story—the stolen cap burns the thief's head. . . . But then, at last, the bridge was empty. He hid in a corner, behind one of the large pillars which supported the bridge, leaned over the balustrade, and peered into the water, as though gazing at something wonderful. With one hand he reached into his pocket, and felt the horrid thing, alive in his fingers. He drew it from his pocket slowly, and opened his hand. The purse was gone.

A circle appeared where the purse had dropped. The circle widened and was followed by others. He watched, hypnotized by the place where his secret had been drowned and buried forever. But suddenly a lovely voice broke into his thoughts, and sweet laughter rang in his ears.

"Any goldfish there? Ha, ha, ha! Why have you been standing and staring into the water for so long?"

Turning about, he saw the cantor's daughter and her friend. Frightened, he asked, "Since when have you been here?"

"All the time, ha, ha, ha!" they answered at once,

laughing. He shuddered, fearing they might have witnessed his act.

Foolish boy! His fears were unfounded. But he was soon to experience another, quite different agony, his role in an unpredictable drama which we shall call "The Cantor's Daughter."

58 The Cantor's Daughter

THE PRIVILEGES OF STUDENTS.   MEETINGS ON THE BRIDGE.
THE DAUGHTER OF CANTOR TZALI.   FALLING IN LOVE.
SHOLOM POURS OUT HIS HEART IN A LETTER.   IT FALLS
INTO BAD HANDS.

In those days, students of county schools were respected in the small towns as much as Gymnasium or university students were in the big cities. Though they did not wear uniforms, they were treated as though they did and were permitted to do all sorts of things that *cheder* children could not. They might play tricks on the beadle, bathe in the river outside the bathhouse, tease whom they pleased, and even talk to girls—although, mind you, the girls had to be of good families. Nor did the girls object to this. Relations between young people at that time were too innocent, however, to be termed flirtations. And the friendship between the cantor's daughter and Sholom was no exception.

It is difficult to recall now, nor does it really matter, just where they first met. Actually it must have been at the bridge, nor could it have been at any other time than Saturday afternoon. Nor is the record clear as to who spoke first. But no doubt one or the other smiled, or perhaps they accidentally brushed against each other. Sholom very likely touched his hat and said, "Good morning," and then, very possibly without touching his hat, added, "How are you?" Thereafter when they met they would stand and chat with each other.

HE: Well, goodbye till next time.

SHE: And when is next time? Next Saturday?

HE: When else?

SHE: Here on the bridge?

HE: Where else?

SHE: Why not somewhere else?

HE: For example?

SHE: Where do you go on *Simchath Torah?*

HE: To the Big Synagogue, naturally.

SHE: Why not to the Cold Synagogue?

HE: Where your father prays?

SHE: So?

HE: My father would miss me.

SHE: Well, if you're afraid of your father. . . .

He was mortified to have her think he was afraid of his father; he had to retrieve this false step, and so he asked if he might speak to her alone, since he had something important to say to her. The cantor's daughter blushed and signaled to her friend to walk on a few steps without her. When they were alone he told her quickly, stuttering as he did so, that he was anxious to see her by herself, without an escort. . . . Was that all he had wanted to say? He must understand her predicament. She too would like to see him in private, but she was never allowed out unchaperoned. However, her friend was no tattle-tale, liked talking to boys herself; as a matter of fact, if he must know, her friend was also in love. "Also in love"—did that mean that the cantor's daughter was in love? Who was she in love with? "If you knew everything," she said, "you'd be an old man."

Nothing further had to be said; he knew whom the cantor's daughter loved. And if there had been any further doubt, he could have told from her face and eyes. It was a sweet face, a face that somehow seemed familiar to him. And the eyes were familiar also. Where had he seen this pale-complexioned girl before? Where had he seen this wavy blond hair? And these hands— these long, slender fingers? It was a small white hand, smooth and warm. For the first time in his life, he held a girl's hand in his.

As a pious Jew impatiently looks forward to the coming of the Messiah, so did Sholom long for *Simchath Torah*. But the holiday was so long in arriving, he thought he would go out of his mind. He decided to write her a letter, although he scarcely knew what impelled him to do it. He spent the whole day and night writing it. The words poured out of him, and the letter would never have ended, had he not run out of paper. Even now he can recall what he said in this first youthful letter and, although he is not a wealthy man, he would pay a nice sum to have it in his possession again.

But, the letter written, the question was how to send it. Clearly there was only one way; it had to be entrusted to her friend. But he scarcely knew her friend. Should a third person be privy to their secret? Worse than that was the fact that he did not know how to reach this third person. Yet there was a way out of this dilemma. To reach the third person, he must employ a fourth person; he had in mind the young man who was loved by the friend of the cantor's daughter. Here there was nothing to worry about; two young men could freely discuss intimacies of this sort. There was only one minor problem—he had to find the fellow and make friends with him.

The young man worked in a hardware store. He was a good-looking fellow, but with huge, massive hands, almost more paws than hands. He was accessible enough but, once having reached him, it wasn't too easy to get the information across. The owner of the store, a woman with dirty hands and a dirty face, could not understand why the son of Nahum Rabinowitz wanted to associate with her salesman, what information the one should have to give to the other. And then, when she had been convinced that there could be such information, no sooner had the salesman learned what Sholom wanted—that is, that he had a request to make of his fiancée—than the salesman began to bristle like a rooster at a cat who has stolen into the chicken coop.

"Who told you I have a fiancée?"

"Her friend."

"Oh, the cantor's daughter. . . . There's a real dish!"

Sholom did not know what a "dish" meant, but he gathered from the salesman's laugh that it was not a compliment.

"What's a dish?"

"Wouldn't you like to know? Tell me, what do you want?"

Sholom took the letter out of his pocket and handed it to the salesman.

"I'd like your fiancée to give this letter to the cantor's daughter and to bring me the reply."

The salesman took the letter and examined it carefully from every conceivable angle.

"Come tomorrow and you'll have your answer."

Now Sholom felt better, but then, the next morning at the stipulated time, the salesman informed him that the answer had not as yet come.

"She'll surely answer you by tomorrow."

But the next day it was the same story. No answer. Sholom noticed that the salesman smiled at him oddly. And he became even more suspicious when the salesman said, "I sure wish I could write like you do."

"How do you know how I write?"

"My fiancée told me."

"Well, how does she know?"

"The cantor's daughter must have told her."

It didn't sound impossible, and Sholom was flattered to receive a compliment from his beloved. But still he wondered, what if the salesman had never delivered the letter, had merely read it himself? But finally the answer did arrive. It was written on a yellow sheet of paper, folded into four parts. No envelope had been used, but the letter had been sealed with wax and stamped with a coin. It was written in long thin characters which reminded him of her slender fingers.

She wrote that she was sorry she could not write as well as he but she had read his letter with tears. If she had wings, she would fly to him. If she had fins, she would swim the oceans to reach him. She could not sleep at night; she was tormented. The only thing she thought about was the holiday. But she warned him not to send future letters through the channels he had used, because she was certain the letter had been opened.

He thought of the salesman's massive paws and turned hot and cold, thinking of them opening the envelope. But then he dismissed the thought from his mind: tomorrow was *Simchath Torah* and he would stand close to the cantor's daughter.

59   The Night of Hakafoth

SORROWS OF YOUNG WERTHER AND THE MAGIC OF HAKAFOTH.
IN THE SYNAGOGUE YARD.   THE FIRST KISS.   THE HEAVENS
OPEN AND ANGELS SING.

If I were Goethe, I would not describe the sorrows of
young Werther; I would describe the sorrows of a poor
Jewish lad who was madly in love with the cantor's
daughter. If I were Heine, I would not sing of Flor-
entine nights; I would sing of the night of *Simchath
Torah,* when Jews make the rounds of *Hakafoth* and
when young women and pretty girls mingle with the
men in the synagogue—the one night when this is permitted. The women kiss the Scroll of the Law. They
jump up and down, squealing in every key, "Long life
to you!" The answer is "Same to you, same to you!"

An hour or two before the *Hakafoth* ceremony, the
smaller children gathered in the synagogue and climbed
upon the benches. Flags fluttered in their hands, flags
topped with red apples in which candles were burning.
But the apples were not redder than the cheeks of the
children, and the candles shone no brighter than their
eyes. The older boys strolled in the synagogue yard,
and there the air was soft and clear, the sky star-
studded, and one had the sensation that the whole
world was enjoying a holiday. Even the silence was
festive, and nothing dared to mar the holiness of this

night, the night of the Rejoicing of the Law, when the Chosen People celebrated the heavenly gift of the Torah throughout the earth.

Did it matter that a peasant cart clattered by, raising a cloud of fragrant dust? Or that the post chaise rumbled past, breaking the stillness with the ting-a-ling of its bells? . . . The dust settled, the sound of the bell died in the distance, and the night remained as holy and as festive as before, for the holiday of the Rejoicing of the Law was being celebrated throughout the world. . . .

A black cat ran past on its soft, velvety paws; it cut across the synagogue yard and disappeared. A dog howled in a melancholy key and then was quiet. Yet the night remained holy, still festive, because this holiday of the Rejoicing of the Law reigned, and it was being celebrated everywhere.

It was easy to breathe in such clear air. One's heart almost burst with joy, and one's soul was light. . . . One felt proud—this was the night of the Rejoicing of the Law! Above was the sky, and God was there—your God, your heaven, your holiday!

"Children, they're starting the *Hakafoth!*"

They darted into the synagogue, but it was a false alarm. The men were still engaged in the evening prayer. Tzali, the cantor of the Cold Synagogue, stood at the altar with his two choir boys: one a swarthy lad with thick lips, the bass; the other a slender boy with a pale face, the soprano. The cantor, Reb Tzali, Tzali of the golden voice, was a tall, blond man with a nose hooked like a bull's horn. He had thin curly earlocks and a blond wavy beard that looked as if it had been tied to his face. Was it possible that this freak had such a handsome daughter? The cantor's daughter, you must understand, was *his* daughter, cantor Tzali was *her* father! . . . His daughter, he often boasted, was unique. There was only one trouble with her—she didn't want to get married. "Anybody we suggest, she turns down. But, of course, that's just nonsense. When the right man comes along, she'll have to say yes. If not, we'll drag her to the wedding by her braids. And of course there's always a cane!" the cantor would say jokingly, flourishing his reed cane with its old yellow ivory knob.

And then at last the evening prayer was finished, but it was still a long way to the *Hakafoth*. Now they were intoning the hymn, "Unto thee it was shown that thou mightest know that the Lord He is God. . . ." Stanzas of the hymn were being distributed among the most distinguished members of the congregation. Everyone recited his stanza, but each in a different key and with a different melody. Actually, the litany was the same the world over, but, since people have different voices and timbres and are a bit frightened of the sound of their own voices, the tune emerged not quite as expected, and the trills which should have come at the end of the stanzas were entirely lost.

The Cold Synagogue was large, wide, and lofty. It had no ceiling—just a roof; that was why it was called the "Cold" Synagogue. The roof was painted sky-blue, but the color was somewhat too blue—in fact, it was almost green. The painter had evidently over-painted it and, besides, had painted the glistening stars a little too large. Each star was only slightly smaller than an apple; they looked rather like potatoes edged with gilt. Nor were they scattered haphazardly like the stars really are; they were painted in orderly rows and crowded together. An ancient candelabrum made of greenish yellow copper hung from the center of the ceiling, suspended by a long copper chain. The candlesticks hanging on the walls were also copper; they were all filled with candles, and every candle was lit. It was dazzling.

Where did all these men come from? All the women, girls, young men, and children? Sholom was visiting the Cold Synagogue for the first time, and he could not help thinking of the verse, "How goodly are thy tents, O Jacob. . . ." It was not easy to find a place. Happily, the beadle recognized him—why, wasn't he the son of Nahum Rabinowitz? Room must be made for him among the members of the congregation on the "mirror" side!

What were they reading now? The noise and confusion were so great that neither the cantor nor the choir boys could be heard. In vain did everyone shout "Quiet!" In vain did the beadle pound his fist on the table. Women were shouting, girls giggling, children squealing. . . .

Here was a little boy crying. "Why are you crying, little boy?" Someone had knocked the apple off his flag and crushed it with his foot. What would he do without an apple? . . . A big boy, standing next to the child, grinned, showing all his teeth. The child's tragedy seemed to amuse him. This annoyed Sholom, and he asked angrily, "What are you laughing at?" The lad replied, still showing all his teeth, "That kid's weak in the head!" His answer irritated Sholom even more. "Were you any brighter at his age?" The fellow stopped grinning. "I really don't remember, but one thing I do know—I have more brains in my heel than you have in your head, even though you do go to the County School and are the son of Nahum Rabinowitz!" Had the son of Nahum Rabinowitz not been among strangers in a strange synagogue, he would have known what to do. But he managed to keep his temper. . . . Besides, through the terrific din, he heard the dear, familiar words with which the beadle invited the congregation to the rite of *Hakafoth.*

"The learned Reb Shimon Zeev, son of Reb Chaim Tzvi, the Cohen, is invited to honor the Torah!"

"The learned Reb Moshe Yaakov, son of Nahman Dov, the Levite, is invited to honor the Torah!"

Each man so honored received a Scroll of the Law with which he paraded around the synagogue.

And so the *Hakafoth* ceremony began. But where was the cantor's daughter? . . .

"O Lord! I beseech thee, save us. . . ." The first round had finished with the chorus "Hai-da!" and with a dance. The beadle again called out in his hoarse voice, "The learned Reb so-and-so is invited to honor the Torah. . . ." Thus ended the second round, the third, the fourth. . . . Each was followed by dancing and singing, and the cantor's daughter was nowhere to be seen!

Sholom could not sit still. He twisted and turned in his seat. Would he ever find her? Could she have deceived him so shabbily? Or had their tryst been discovered and had she been kept at home under lock and key? One could expect anything of Cantor Tzali, a man capable of pulling a girl by her braids and caning her! . . .

Apparently the beadle, noticing Sholom squirming in his seat and looking restlessly about, thought he must be eager to be called. Or perhaps it was one of the trustees who wanted to give Rabinowitz's son a treat. In any event, Sholom suddenly heard his name called. "Sholom, the son of Manahem Nahum, is invited to honor the Torah!"

The blood rushed to his head. All eyes seemed to be fixed upon him. He felt as every young man feels when he is summoned for the first time to read from the Torah. Almost before he knew it, the beadle had brought a Scroll to him, and, standing among the others, he hugged the large Scroll in his arms. The procession had already begun. Cantor Tzali, at the head, sang, "Helper of the poor, save us!" Women and girls crowded about to kiss the Scrolls, calling out, "Long life to you!" It was strange to be treated with so much respect. The unexpected honor thrilled Sholom. He was very proud to be the only youth among men—and all because he was somebody. He was the son of Nahum Rabinowitz! . . . Suddenly someone kissed his hand. "Long life to you!" He raised his eyes and saw the cantor's daughter, standing next to her friend. . . .

The heavens opened; angels descended singing hymns. They praised the world God had created—this good, beautiful world; praised the people He had created—good, kind people! Everything was so beautiful, Sholom wanted to weep, and his heart sang to the angels.

He was astonished and bewildered—instead of kissing the Scroll, she had kissed his hand. Had it been an accident? It could not have been! Her smiling eyes told him. He almost dropped the Scroll. He wanted to pause, to look again into her eyes, to say a word or two. . . . But he could not. He had to move on. The Scroll had to be passed to another. Only when he had reached the altar and returned the Scroll to the beadle was he able to glance back. But she was no longer there. Again he was in the procession, straggling after the men, but this time without a Scroll. His eyes searched for her everywhere, but she had disappeared. Perhaps it had only been an illusion. But he still felt the kiss on his hand. As he left the synagogue, he felt that he had wings; he was flying. . . . Angels were flying with him.

In the Big Synagogue, the ceremony was still going on. Father was in high spirits. Dressed in an old satin coat which was cracked at the seams, showing its yellow lining in places, he nevertheless looked noble and handsome. Lazar Yossel and Magidov stood beside him. Father smiled as he listened to them. "Where have you been?" he asked Sholom, not angrily, but out of curiosity. "In the Cold Synagogue," Sholom replied, and boasted that his name had been called to honor the Torah. "That was very nice of them!" Father said, pleased, and the superior sons-in-law teased Sholom. One of them asked whether he had been introduced to the

Helper of the Poor. The other remarked, "How could he have met the Helper there? It's only the Helper's grandson who's at the Cold Synagogue!" Everyone laughed. What a night that was! Such a night could only come during *Simchath Torah!*

60 The Crisis

BETRAYED.   TYPHOID.   A NEW PERSON LEAVES THE SICK-
BED.   FAREWELL TO CHILDHOOD.

He was not destined to remain floating in the heavens. Shortly after this first ascent, there came a dreadful disappointment and he came crashing down to earth. One might have anticipated that their families would discover the clumsy romance and break it up, that Cantor Tzali would drag his daughter off by the braids or even cane her. . . . But who would have dreamt that all the while the cantor's daughter was flirting with Sholom, she was having a romance with a Gentile, a clerk in Katelnikov's hardware store, or that one Saturday night, not long after the memorable holiday, she would elope, be baptized, and marry the clerk!

Poor Cantor Tzali rushed around the city seeking help. He sought the intervention of the Archimandrite, the Abbess, and even the Governor. But nothing availed, and the city went wild; the world had turned upside down. . . . Had she been just anyone, one might have said, "Oh, well, there's nothing to do about it. Bad luck!" But, no! It had happened to a *cantor's* daughter. Who would now allow the cantor to approach the altar? The whole congregation shared his shame. Why had it happened to *their* cantor, the cantor of *their* synagogue? . . .

But their sorrow and shame were nothing compared to the hell endured by the boy who had been madly in love with the cantor's daughter—the boy whom she had deceived, whom she had left for a Gentile! Why had she deceived him, written him love letters, kissed his hand, sworn undying love? . . . Surely the elopement had not been due to some sudden passion. The elopement must have been planned a long time before. Sholom recalled what her friend's fiancée had called her—a dish. Now he knew what a dish was. And the thought made him so angry that he cursed himself and the day he had met the cantor's daughter, as well as the hardware store, Katelnikov's clerk, and all the clerks in the world. . . . How happy he would have been if an immense fire had wiped out all the hardware stores in the city, if a hurricane had swept even the shops and the houses away, if the earth had opened and swallowed up the city of Pereyaslov, along with its bridge and its brook and its suburbs—as had happened in the story of Korah. Sholom was merciless. He felt pity for neither his dear ones nor those he did not know; not even the thought of children moved him. Let them all perish, let them all drop down to hell!

For the world that God had created was a false, ugly world, and the people that God had created were false, ugly people. . . .

One day, he returned from school with his head full of such misanthropic reflections. He felt dazed, and circles and triangles and rhomboids flashed before his eyes. The circles disintegrated, the triangles melted like snow in the sun, and then new circles and triangles took their places. He refused food. Stepmother made her usual pleasantry, "Has the world gone mad?" But Sholom couldn't stand on his feet. He had to lie down on the couch, and Father came to him, felt his forehead, and asked him something. Sholom replied, but he hadn't the slightest idea what he was saying—he had forgotten both question and answer. Then he was being fed something bitter out of a teaspoon—something that smelled of almonds. . . . His head, oh, his head! . . . Now balls were floating before his eyes; they passed through his ears and floated away with a long-drawn-out whistle. Prickles rose beneath his skin; they tickled, boiled, and bubbled in his body—and purses, countless purses, went rolling downhill. . . . Running after them were people vainly trying to catch them. Although his eyes were shut, he could somehow see all that went on. He could not hear anything because of the whistling in his ears, but he could see everything. Everyone was there, an assortment of old and new friends, and unknown people as well. Shmulik was there, and Pinneleh, Elie, Uncle Pinney's son Itzel, and the lodger Wolfson. . . . They were all there. But, strangest of all, Katelnikov's clerk was praying before the altar, singing, "Unto thee it was shown . . ." and the cantor's daughter was beating her breast, "For my sins, for my sins!" A cry, a hollow stifled cry, issued from the Cold Synagogue, and strange, wailing voices sobbed. The corpses were praying. Everyone knew that every Sabbath night corpses prayed in the Cold Synagogue. . . .

Nothing astonished Sholom, not even a Gentile clerk singing, "Unto thee it was shown . . ." to the correct tune. But one thing did perplex him—how was it that Shmulik the Orphan did not ask him about the treasure? Could he have forgotten such an important thing? Sholom opened his eyes to look for Shmulik, but could not find him. He had vanished, and so had the others. Where had they gone? He shut his eyes and listened to the beating of his heart and the pounding in his temples. He felt soaked with perspiration; he was swimming in a river of sweat. The tips of his fingers were wrinkled, as after a steam bath; his hair was wet and clung to his forehead. A cold hand touched him, and he heard a familiar sigh. He opened his eyes. Father was there, and next to him Wolfson, and The Collector in his black spectacles among a number of others. Everyone was looking at him compassionately, and he heard them say, "Crisis!" He did not understand, but he was very pleased suddenly to be the center of attention. Father bent over his bed and asked, "What would you like?" Sholom did not answer immediately. He first wanted to get his bearings and to understand what was happening to him. It took him several minutes to realize that he had been sick, very sick, and now, it seemed, he was better. Better? Why, he felt marvelous!

Then he licked his dry lips with his tongue and uttered a word, one single word.

"Gooseberry!"

Father looked at the others and then asked him, "Gooseberry? What gooseberry?"

"Jam!" the sick boy answered with an unfamiliar bass that began with a high note and sank to the depths. He was startled—he could not recognize his own voice. . . .

During his illness he had changed so greatly that, when he left his bed some weeks later and dragged himself into the hall and looked into the mirror, he could scarcely recognize himself. A stranger stood before him. He had once been a pretty boy with fat red cheeks. He had once been agile, lively, and bright-eyed; his hair had been cut low, and a wavy blond curl had fallen over his forehead. Now he was pale. His cheeks were hollow, his eyes had grown larger, their gaze was more serious. He seemed to have been stretched—he was much taller than before. His curly blond hair had been shaved off like a Tartar's.

The change in him was not only external. He had altered inwardly. It was as if his soul, too, had gone through a crisis, and now he regretted his foolish, naive past which would never return.

And he stood there re-living the past and, as he paused at the edge of the future, he bade his childhood farewell, forever.